Douglas Weiss, Ph.D.

Recovery
For Everyone

Workbook

Recovery for Everyone: Workbook
© 2014 by Douglas W. Weiss, Ph.D.
P.O. Box 51055
Colorado Springs, CO 80949

ISBN #978-1-881292-06-7

Interior and Cover Design By: Janelle Evangelides

Contents

Part Two: Personal Growth Recovery Techniques

Part Three: Maintaining Recovery Techniques

Introduction

Recovery for Everyone: Workbook has been written for Christians who struggle with addiction and desire techniques to assist them throughout the different development stages of their recovery. As a recovering addict with more than 25 years of successful recovery, my personal recovery journey has educated me immensely about the recovery process. I personally have practiced many of the exercises in the pages ahead. Additionally, as a therapist, researcher, author and lecturer on the subject of addiction, I have compiled these exercises and principles, which have successfully helped many addicts to begin and maintain their recovery from addiction.

These exercises are listed in the chronological order recommended for the progression of the addict's recovery. The journey of recovery teaches us "first things first." I encourage you not to pick and choose which exercises you will or will not do, but rather receive from each exercise the insight it has to offer as you complete the exercise.

This book can most certainly be used in conjunction with therapy or as part of a 12-step or church support group. My hope is you receive the precious gift of recovery Jesus Christ has to offer, as I have, and maintain it the rest of your life for your benefit and for the benefit of others.

If we can be of any service along the way, feel free to write to Heart to Heart Counseling Center, P.O. Box 51055, Colorado Springs, Colorado 80949 or call (719) 278-3708. You can also visit our website at drdougweiss.com. Some of our materials related to addiction include books, DVDs and CDs. Support products are also available for wives in a relationship with an addict. Telephone counseling is available for those who want to counsel with Dr. Weiss or an independent therapist trained by Dr. Weiss. We are available to minister to the church body as well through training seminars. For more in depth services, see the appendix of this book. We look forward to helping you become and stay free from addiction. If God calls you into this ministry of healing, and you would like to start a recovery group in your church, see the appendix of this workbook to learn how you can begin a recovery group. If you do start a group, please notify our office so we can refer those who call us and are in need of a group.

Douglas Weiss, Ph.D.

Part 1

Beginning Recovery Techniques

#1
Daily Time For Recovery

Recovering from addiction will be one of the hardest undertakings in an addict's life. In the midst of their addiction, the typical addict has clocked in hundreds, and sometimes thousands, of hours of repetitive, addictive conditioning. Many addicts rely heavily upon their addictive acting out, as a primary coping mechanism before beginning the journey of recovery.

Recovery is hard work, and more importantly, it is consistent work. Remember, it took consistent behaviors to spiral you into your addiction. It only makes sense that consistent work is going to be a big part of your recovery and reconditioning yourself into a life of recovery from addiction.

In light of this, you are going to need time to practice many of the exercises in this workbook daily, which will enhance your recovery process. These exercises have been successfully proven to work, but only if you take the time to do them. This is consistent with the fact that in most areas of life, what you put into something is also what you get out. So, you may need to have a daily calendar and try to come up with at least 15 to 30 minutes a day to work on your recovery from addiction. This effort will make a big difference on the length of time it will take you to experience recovery. This, of course, is not the total amount of time you will need to work your recovery, as we will discuss later about attending support groups. Scheduling these support group meetings on your calendar will also be a <u>very</u> important part of your recovery from addiction!

My daily time for recovery is from _____ to _____

_____
Your signature

_____
Spouse's Signature (if applicable)

#2
Cleaning House

The information in this exercise may be obvious to many Christian addicts, but for the benefit of those who have never read anything about achieving recovery from addiction, this exercise must be discussed. "Cleaning house" at the beginning of your recovery will steer you from keeping that "one" thing from your addiction, which could possibly cause you to relapse down the road. Many addicts I have counseled with had their first relapse with the one thing they didn't throw away.

To prevent this experience from happening later, it is imperative to throw away (don't try to sell or inflict this material on anyone else) any item, which could cause you to relapse. This could be any thing from empty bottles to music or pictures from acting out. You'll know what this is and you can ask God to help you here.

You also will want to guard against any technology that you used during your addiction. Many addicts have relapsed through relationships or social network sites.

In the beginning of your recovery, it is much better to error on the side of being too cautious, than to error on the side of not being cautious enough. Some of the more restrictive boundaries can be changed to less restrictive boundaries in the future when your recovery is not as fragile as it is in the beginning.

This exercise can be a great beginning for your recovery. If you feel you need help, you may want to ask a friend or support group member, who has some stable sobriety, if they can be supportive through this exercise. For some addicts, cleaning house is a new beginning. It's a time you mark as the beginning of your journey. This is a great way to start your recovery and remove some of the possibilities for future stumbles.

The date I totally cleaned house was _____

#3
Early Prayer

Prayer is something many addicts even Christians find difficult to do, especially if they have avoided God because of the shame and guilt of their behavior or possibly what was done to them in the past. Prayer is simply a behavior that, when put in place, can change the addict's disposition. We know from other addictions that an addiction is basically self-will run riot. This expression of addiction is basically "doing your own thing," which is not very helpful for the Christian addict's recovery.

Take time out to pray first thing in the morning. If you need help, just use the guidelines of the Lord's Prayer (Matthew 6:9-13). During your prayer time, do not forget to ask Jesus to help you stay sober, accountable and honest today, so you can stay free from addiction. He is proud of you for starting your recovery. His death purchased your freedom. Your prayer can help you realize this on a daily basis.

Prayer is a way for you to behaviorally change yourself. For many addicts, addiction starts early in the day, not necessarily the first thing in the morning but maybe in the shower, on the way to work or while driving. Prayer is preventative. It is a way of acknowledging you are an addict and are in desperate need of Christ's freedom. Without sobriety, the addict is on a path of self-destruction, not only in his own life but more than likely those around him have been devastated, either through their anger, depression or acting-out behavior.

The addict is in a fight every day, especially the first 30 to 90 days, which is the toughest part of recovery for the recovering addict. So, make sure you connect with Jesus. Your prayer doesn't have to be long. Prayer may or may not make you feel better instantly, but it is one of the Five Commandments, which we will be discussing in a later exercise. If you begin to apply them to your life, you will begin to reap the benefits. As a Christian, prayer is one of the many tools you can have in your search for recovery from addiction.

The time in the morning I can pray is _____

#4
Reading Recovery Material

Reading recovery material that specifically relates to your specific addiction is so important. There are currently several Christian books on the market addressing addictions. It is very important to read some recovery material every day.

It is best to read in the morning. Addicts need to be reminded of what may be in store for them that day. Sometimes, the recovery thoughts you have just read about are the very tools that will help you out of a tough situation, such as a fantasy. Those tools will give you the strength to fight for your recovery that day. It is important you involve your mind during your journey for recovery. I realize some people are not big readers. I would encourage you to read recovery material or obtain CDs or DVDs on recovery you can listen to. Some people listen to recovery-type CDs in their car, and this has helped them keep their mind focused on their recovery. It alone is not going to save you, but it may help you behave so you can maintain your abstinent behaviors and not pass your bottom line. A list of reading materials is provided in an exercise you will be reading about later.

By now, you probably have a feeling your morning is going to change. This can take 5 to 15 minutes and will make a dramatic change in your day. You are worth getting the recovery you need, so you can restore yourself, your family and friends. You are going to learn a lot, not only about yourself but also about recovery in general, so you can get a picture of hope to integrate into a lifestyle of sobriety.

Reading your Bible is great to do on a daily basis. As a Christian, this will strengthen your spirit. Reading the Bible is not a substitute for educating yourself about addiction. Ignorance regarding addiction has probably cost you a lot of guilt and shame already. Informing yourself about it is a responsible behavior, such as a diabetic would study up on diabetes. Daily recovery reading is critical, especially in the first 90 days of your recovery.

My daily reading time will be _____

#5
Call Someone

A phone call can be the very thing that may save you from an acting-out experience today. The first step of the Twelve Steps talks about the word "we." "We" means you need someone else in your program to help you. In the past, "I" has been the biggest focus in the addict's world. Previously, the addict didn't have the resources to receive help due to their powerlessness. In being powerless, addicts couldn't fight addiction alone. What the addict can do is involve others in the fight to dissipate the energy that comes against their life to destroy it. Addiction cannot be dealt with alone. I have not experienced, nor have I known any one else who has experienced, recovery from addiction ALONE.

As a Christian, you know the body has many parts. You need another person to be accountable to and check in with. Remember James 5:16, "...confess your faults...so you may be healed." The reverse is also true. Keep your faults (secret thoughts, behaviors) to yourself, and you will stay sick! Many addicts have years of research on staying sick. You must push past your comfort zone to become and stay healthy. There are no lone rangers in the Christian walk, and there are definitely no lone rangers in achieving recovery from addiction. Remember, if you humble yourself, you can be free. If you do not, humiliation will await you, whether anyone finds out about your behavior or not.

A lifestyle of sobriety is a much greater goal than just being abstinent. There are several ways to address this commandment about making phone calls. One way is to wait until you get into a crisis, and then call someone to help you. This method does not work, because if you don't have a relationship with anyone, you are putting up a barrier that could isolate you. Making a phone call and saying "I am an addict" is a big enough task all by itself to accomplish, let alone having to tell someone you have never talked to before you are close to acting out in some manner.

When you are not alone, you are accountable. The way to begin making phone calls is to make one call in the morning to another recovering addict. Tell them you are not in trouble, but if you do get in trouble, you are going to call someone today. If you are checked in with someone, eventually the phone calls are going to turn into conversations, which develop healthy relationships.

Addicts need relationships. Part of your re-socialization is making phone calls, feeling connected and getting acceptance right at the beginning of the day. If you can make a phone call early in the morning to someone else in the program, you are going to find strength in your day. Like prayer, the phone is a tool you can use to help yourself get stronger, especially within the first 30 to 90 days when you are going to need other people to help you more than ever before. The people you call will benefit just as much, if not more than you will, when you call them. Make a phone call every day. You don't need to philosophically agree with this concept or have a good feeling about it to decide if you are going to do it. This phone call behavior is so that you can get free today.

I will call _____(name) at _____(time)

#6
Going To Support Groups

In Alcoholics Anonymous, there is an old expression that says "There are three times when you should go to a meeting, when you don't feel like going to a meeting, when you do feel like going to a meeting and at eight o'clock." It is not a matter of how you feel about it. It is how you behave about it. In Twelve Step meetings, there is a "ninety-meetings-in-ninety-days" principle. This principle is ideal. Even in most major metropolitan areas I know there are not meetings every day of the week. In the midst of a tough situation, where you are far removed from a metropolitan area, it can be more difficult. If this happens to you, you may want to consider talking with someone in a meeting about getting together with them more frequently as an option. There are Christians in many of these meetings.

If you are interested in starting a Recovery Group in your church, please contact us, so we can refer people to your group. See our Recovery Group information in the Appendix section of this workbook. If it isn't possible to start a Recovery Group, and there are none available in your area, you may have to attend a traditional support group, which you can find on the internet. It is our belief that God wants to use His church to heal those struggling with addiction in the church, as well as in the community. If the church will open their healing doors, I believe we will see no less than a revival!

These meetings are basically to support you, and at some point, give back to others what you have learned through your own particular journey of recovery. Being around other recovering addicts is going to help you. First, it is going to give you hope as you see other addicts having successful sobriety. Second, if they can do it, you may believe you can too. You can learn things from them, which they have learned through negative or positive experiences. I want to encourage you to attend to as many meetings as possible.

The meetings I will make are:

Day _____   Time _____

Day _____   Time _____

Day _____   Time _____

#7
Evening Prayer

Praying again in the evening may sound redundant. You can read Exercise #3, Early Prayer again to be reminded this is not something you have to like or even agree with. Prayer is something that is best to do twice, minimally, every day. At the end of the day, if you are sober, thank God for keeping you sober that day. Every day of recovery is a miracle to personally thank Jesus for.

Recovery from addiction isn't something you do by yourself. It is something you do with the help of God and others. If there is any other issue from the day you want to talk to God about, you can also bring them up at this time. If you don't have a relationship with God, ask Him to open your relationship and bring people into your life to bring this about. It is important to begin and end your day in a spiritual place. The recovery program that is going to work is spiritual in nature. Since you were born spirit, soul and body, it is important to reestablish your own spirituality. Many addicts don't nurture their spiritual component, even though they are Christians. Make this a time to be thankful you had a day of recovery. Even the worst day in recovery is something to be thankful for. Even your best day without recovery, you were covered with shame, guilt and fear. So, if you have any relief from those feelings, I believe it is appropriate to respond in prayer.

#8
The Five Commandments
A 90-Day Checklist

Recovery from addiction has some basic principles that when applied help the addict sustain their recovery program. Early recovery is not simply understanding the facts, nor is early recovery simply talking about addiction. Recovery goes much deeper than simply talking about what was done in the past. Many Christians may talk about getting better. The Prodigal Son, who was probably an alcoholic, did not get better or become restored once he realized he was in a bad condition. He had to consistently walk back to receive the blessings of his recovery after weeks or months of walking. Then the party started, not before.

The Five Commandments are simple and can be put up on your wall or mirror at home. Write the commandments down, and check off if you have done them today, this week, this month and the first 90 days. The behavioral checklist assures you are putting behavioral steps toward recovery, as opposed to just coming to an understanding about addiction. Coming to an understanding is not the only answer for the addict. You may have been in pain for years and possibly have had behaviors you have repeated hundreds of times. It is for this reason the Five Commandments, when put in place, can provide an action plan, so you can begin to arrest the addiction you may have been struggling with for so long.

Simply put, the Five Commandments are the last five behaviors you have read about in Exercise #3 through #7.

These Five Commandments are simple:

The Five Commandmentes
1 Pray in the morning
2 Read recovery literature daily
3 Meetings-Attend Twelve-Step Meetings or Recovery Groups
4 Call someone in recovery
5 Pray again and thank God for sobriety

The checklist on the following page will help you monitor your behaviors toward recovery. When it comes to recovery, remember only believe your behaviors. Don't talk yourself into believing if you feel free, you are. Behave free and you will be.

Date	Pray	Read	Meet	Call	Pray	Date	Pray	Read	Meet	Call	Pray
1.						46.					
2.						47.					
3.						48.					
4.						49.					
5.						50.					
6.						51.					
7.						52.					
8.						53.					
9.						54.					
10.						55.					
11.						56.					
12.						57.					
13.						58.					
14.						59.					
15.						60.					
16.						61.					
17.						62.					
18.						63.					
19.						64.					
20.						65.					
21.						66.					
22.						67.					
23.						68.					
24.						69.					
25.						70.					
26.						71.					
27.						72.					
28.						73.					
29.						74.					
30.						75.					
31.						76.					
32.						77.					
33.						78.					
34.						79.					
35.						80.					
36.						81.					
37.						82.					
38.						83.					
39.						84.					
40.						85.					
41.						86.					
42.						87.					
43.						88.					
44.						89.					
45.						90.					

#9
Maximized Thinking

The maximized thinking technique is easy to understand. Simply ask yourself daily, especially during the first year of recovery, "Is this the most I can put into my recovery today?" If the answer is more "yes" than "no," you will find yourself progressing through recovery quite well. Maximized thinking plays a big part in early recovery.

Those who consistently maintain the Five Commandments, which you learned about in the previous exercise, as much as possible, will make tremendous gains with maximized thinking added to their personal, spiritual, sexual and financial lifestyle. I have seen many addicts who have chosen maximized thinking in their recovery that have doubled their income in their first year, as well as experienced a much healthier social, spiritual and sexual lifestyle.

Other options are shades of minimized thinking, asking yourself, "How little can I do?" In order to show others you are trying to recover. This type of minimized thinking is done mostly on a less-than-conscious level and can be measured by a lack of recovery behaviors.

One way I determine the addict's level of seriousness in early recovery is by their recovery behaviors. Intention, no matter how good, misleads you to think you are in recovery when you actually are not. The Five Commandments is a good way to determine if you are applying maximized thinking or some other approach to what may be the hardest task of your life, recovering from addiction. If you are still reading up to this point, that is a good sign, but keep on going! Your life can be 10 to 100 times better than any day living actively in an addicted lifestyle. Trust me when I say, "you are worth your recovery." Nobody deserves their recovery from addiction without effort, and nobody I know receives it that way either. So, maximize the early part of your recovery, and you will have the rest of your life to thank yourself for the time you invested in the beginning of your recovery journey.

Remember, you have not resisted sin unto death as Christ has for us. Think, "What is the best I can do to become and stay free for Him, since He has given His best for me."

#10
Objective Measures

Having an objective measure can help you realize when you are in the process of recovery. Objective measures can also help you to reestablish trust with your spouse and others that are important to you. You can incorporate an objective measure on a somewhat consistent basis to verify your recovery up to that point in time. Let me give you some examples of objective measures.

1.	Alcoholic	Breathalyzer test or blood work
2.	Debt	Credit reports
3.	Sex	Polygraph test
4.	Food	Scale
5.	Drug	Drug test

These objective measures are your friends. They keep you and everyone around you in reality. Not the reality you want to believe but true reality. I find addicts who incorporate an objective measure significantly increases their chances at getting and staying free for a lifetime.

#11
Retraining The Brain

As an addict, your brain has been conditioned neurologically to your acting-out behaviors. Many addicts were exposed to their addiction at a young age. Every time the addict acted out, they sent positive reinforcements to their brain. The brain, as an organ of the body, has no morality. It just knows when it receives a rush of what I call "brain cookies" or chemicals, it feels good. The rush could be from heroin, sky diving, sex or cocaine. Regardless of what caused the rush, the brain, as an organ, would not have a moral dilemma on how it received this rush.

After frequent conditioning, the addict begins to develop neurological pathways in the brain from acting out. The brain, as an organ, adjusts to getting its neurological need met by the cycle of acting out.

To recover from addiction, you must retrain your brain to not connect acting out thoughts with these so called "brain cookies." To stop this biological cycle that the addict has had in place anywhere from 10 to 50 years, they will need a biological reconditioning cycle. One way is to place a rubber band on either wrist, and when you start to have acting out thoughts, snap the rubber band on the inside of your wrist. This sets up a cycle in your brain that says "acting out thoughts - pain" instead of "acting out thoughts - pleasure." The body is designed to avoid pain, and so this will reduce the amount of acting out thoughts you are having and eventually lessen the inappropriate thoughts, so you can focus on your recovery. You can memorize and quote appropriate scriptures to strengthen your spirit when you snap the rubber band, but use the rubber band to recondition your brain.

The average person who is very consistent with this reconditioning exercise of the brain finds about 80% of the acting out thoughts subsides within the first 30 days. If continued throughout the first 90 days, they find intruding thoughts are minimal and manageable with other exercises discussed later. This is a great exercise to truly "take your thoughts captive." You deserve a clean thought life and a retrained brain, and with consistency, you can achieve it. This exercise is a very effective tool for the early part of your recovery from addiction.

I placed the rubber band on my wrist _____ (Date)

Beginner's Bibliotherapy

I am grateful that so many Christians have been writing on a variety of addictions for years now. I have no way of listing every book on every addiction. I would encourage you to start a beginners bibliography. You can ask your recovery group members, pastor or just Google "Christian _____" (name of addiction) and you will probably come up with some more as well. Christian book websites can also be helpful for this as well. Then start reading regularly the recovery books you find.

People I can ask	Books I found
1. _____	1. _____
2. _____	2. _____
3. _____	3. _____
4. _____	4. _____
5. _____	5. _____

#13
The Three-Second Rule

The three-second rule is simple. When applied, it can stop the Christian addict from beginning a fantasy about acting out before it happens. If you are looking at something in an inappropriate manner, count to three, and then turn away. DON'T look back! I realize some of you think and process very quickly, so for you, the one-second rule would apply. For instant scanners, don't even count to one. Look away instantly! This works great, especially in public places like malls, restaurants or driving.

The "no turning back" is the hardest part. If you stick with this, it is easier for fantasies to subside, and it reduces the cruising around "for a better look" or making contact with the person. In a way, this is rubbernecking in reverse. Instead of stretching to see what or who you are looking at, you count to three or less, and stretch your neck to look at something else in the other direction that is safer for you and your recovery from addiction. This will probably add a lot more time to your schedule too!

Do whatever you have to do to personalize this exercise to work best for you in order to stay free from your addiction.

#14
Pray For Those Who Tempt Us

As an addict, you may have participated in relationships that supported your addiction. If you are an alcoholic, you probably had drinking buddies. Drug addicts have using buddies. Codependents have someone to help, rescue, or use them inappropriately. Sex addicts have porn or sex partners. If you are an overworker you had other people who overworked along side of you. You get the picture.

Addicts tend to build support for their values and beliefs around their particular addiction. In classic recovery the addict is told to change their play places and playmates. This would include others that you might like and who have cared for you in some way, however they will be dangerous for you to be around.

You may need to block their phone numbers and e-mails but whatever you do, you must take a significant and possibly a permanent hiatus from that relationship. For now, when you think about them or want to reach out to them, pray for them. If they run into you, ask to pray for them. If they need anything refer them to your group leader.

Below list the people you will probably need to change in your life for the best chance for you to stay free from your addiction.

1. _____   6. _____

2. _____   7. _____

3. _____   8. _____

4. _____   9. _____

5. _____   10. _____

#15
Memorize

As a Christian over time, you've probably heard someone talking about memorizing scripture. Memorizing scripture is also very helpful if not essential for the recovering person. All of you utilizing this workbook have different addictions. We all do well to follow the command in Romans 12:2 to not conform to this world (addiction) but transform your mind. As you memorize scripture, you may strengthen the very spirit of God within you.

You can place the appropriate scripture in your cell phone by text, e-mail or note section. You can even record them on your phone and listen to them. Daily scripture memory is making great use of your recovery mind. If you don't know the scriptures well, you can ask your support group leader for some helpful scriptures to memorize.

Below list five recovery people's favorite scripture.

Name   Scripture

1. _____   1. _____

2. _____   2. _____

3. _____   3. _____

4. _____   4. _____

5. _____   5. _____

#16
Triggers

Every addiction is unique in how it could externally trigger you to want to reengage your addiction. For the codependent it might be a person in need. For an alcoholic it might be a beer commercial. For the drug addict it could be some drug paraphernalia you found. For the sex addict it could be an open internet connection or a perceived interest from someone.

It would be best for you to be aware of what or who could trigger you to want to engage your addiction.

Below list these things that are possible triggers for you and what you can do to avoid these.

Triggers	Plan
1. _____	1. _____
2. _____	2. _____
3. _____	3. _____
4. _____	4. _____
5. _____	5. _____

#17
Where Not To Go

Addiction and boundaries do not mix very well together. In your acting-out days, you probably would not be able to recognize a boundary if you tripped over one. In your addiction recovery lifestyle, it will be very important for you to set some limitations for your own safety and recovery. Boundaries simply establish some guidelines for places you do not need to go. As long as you stay within your boundaries, you can be safer from your addiction than if you don't have a conscious list of boundaries.

List below the places you believe could hinder your recovery from addiction. See the example.

Example	Your List
1. Adult Bookstore	1. _____
2. Dealers House	2. _____
3. Ex Boyfriend/Girlfriend Place	3. _____
4. Bar	4. _____
5. Work after 5 p.m.	5. _____
	6. _____
	7. _____
	8. _____
	9. _____
	10._____

The more cautious the list of boundaries in early recovery, the more it may keep you from slipping.

#18
Who I Shouldn't See

Talking about boundaries with someone else can be uncomfortable. Most people want to be liked by everybody. An addict, whether knowingly or unknowingly, surrounds themselves many times with other addicts. This makes it difficult as you decide whom you should not see during early recovery. You may ask, "Do I have to give up all my friends?" Hopefully, not all your friends are linked to your addiction, although, some may not be in your best interest to spend time with. You can refer to your earlier start at this on the exercise "Pray For Those Who Tempt Us."

Setting boundaries around people you should not see may be necessary for the first 90 days only. For some people, however, you truly do have to look at possibly ending those relationships. No friend is worth the shame, guilt, lack of intimacy and staying addicted. No real friend would ask that of you. Remember, "Can two walk together unless they are agreed?" (Amos 3:3), and "Bad company corrupts good morals" (I Cor. 15:33b).

In considering boundaries around people you should not see, ask yourself the following questions.

1. Have I acted out with this person in a sexual way in the past?
2. Am I being grooming by this person for an addiction?
3. Have I had an inappropriate romantic/sexual relationship with this person in the past?
4. Does this person have my drug of choice accessible if I visit them?
5. Do I think this person may be an addict?
6. Could I relapse around this person?
7. Have I gone with this person to places on my "where not to go" boundary list?

Answering "yes" to one or more of these questions may make this person a risk to your recovery. With as much honesty as you can, try to fill in the columns below. Run this list by another recovering person tho help you make this exercise as clear as possible

People I Know I Can't Be With	Try-and-See People	Safe People to Be With
1. _____	1. _____	1. _____
2. _____	2. _____	2. _____
3. _____	3. _____	3. _____
4. _____	4. _____	4. _____
5. _____	5. _____	5. _____

#19
Boundaries: Entertainment

Television Boundaries

Television presents some real dilemmas for addicts. The current pop culture is a highly addictive one. The increase of sexually explicit scenes that involve your addiction on television and movie screens can trigger the addict into a myriad of thoughts and behaviors. This does not even include the issue of commercials or the talk shows, which are often about people's lives who are out of control in some manner. Remember, Lot "Vexed his righteous soul by seeing and hearing unrighteousness" (II Peter 2:7-8). Vexed or tormented is exactly what can happen to the Christian addict who is exposed to addiction on television, especially cable television.

Television is not a safe place for addicts, especially during the early part of their recovery. Listed below are various boundaries many addicts in my practice have chosen in order to maintain a successful recovery.

1. No television at all for the first 90 days of recovery
2. Pre-selected television shows only
3. No channel surfing
4. Mute the commercials
5. No talk shows
6. No watching television alone
7. No television in the bedroom
8. Only watch television with family in the family room
9. No television past a certain time (10 p.m. or 11 p.m.)
10. No television in the middle of the night
11. No cable television within the first 90 days of recovery
12. No cable television at all
13. No pay-per-view television

In the following spaces, you may want to list your television boundaries for the next 90 days.

If I relapse once due to a television experience, I will _____

If I relapse twice due to a television experience, I will _____

If I relapse three times due to a television experience, I will _____

The person I will be accountable to for my television boundaries and consequence is

_____

I will check in on this issue with the above person:

Daily	Weekly	Bimonthly

Movie and DVD Boundaries

Movies/DVDs are a dangerous place for addicts trying hard to recover successfully. The movie theater can be a nightmare if you don't have boundaries in place. I cannot begin to tell you how many stories I have heard of precious recovery being damaged by an addict without predetermined movie boundaries.

Movies/DVDs are a great form of entertainment and can be enjoyed in a safe manner, even for addicts. I myself enjoy movies, but like other successful recovering addicts, only with firm boundaries. Also, for home DVD viewing, you can purchase an electronic device, which removes nudity, sexual contact, blasphemy and curse words. For more information, visit clearplay.com. Listed below are some of the boundaries addicts in my practice have utilized in order to maintain sobriety.

1. No movies within the first 90 days of recovery
2. No X or R-rated movies
3 No R-rated movies for the first 90 days of recovery
4. No PG-13 or R-rated movies (PG-13 can have full nudity.)
5. Only go to movies I would take a child to see (PG or G-rated movies)
6. Read movie reviews in paper and avoid "nudity" or "adult-situation" movies or addiction issues
7 Watch only DVDs with a blocker

Fill in the spaces below listing your movie/DVD boundaries.

My movie and DVD boundaries are:

_____   _____

_____   _____

_____   _____

If I relapse once due to a movie/DVD, I will _____

If I relapse twice due to a movie/DVD, I will _____

If I relapse three times due to a movie/DVD, I will _____

The person I will be accountable to for my movie/DVD boundaries is _____

I will check in on my movie/DVD boundaries:

Daily	Weekly	Bimonthly

Magazine Boundaries

Being the visual creatures that many addicts are, magazines can stimulate them into unhealthy thoughts. Magazines have made addiction of various types seem glamorous. Magazines are created to get you into a fantasy state, so you buy their products. The magazines I am talking about are pop magazines, not pornography magazines. Hopefully, this is already a set boundary.

Whether it be a mailed magazine, catalogue or one purchased at a store, you may want to set a boundary to also include catalogs. Even men's and women's fashion and health magazines are riddled with inappropriate stories and advertisements, so think about the appropriateness of these materials as well. If you are choosing to recover successfully, be honest with yourself, as far as the ones you can and cannot participate in. Your boundaries may change in the future as you move further along in recovery, but let's fill in the chart below now. Discontinued magazines

Magazines I can read	Magazines I can't read	Due to a relapse
_____	_____	_____
_____	_____	_____
_____	_____	_____
_____	_____	_____
_____	_____	_____

#20
Boundaries: Internet

The internet is now an integral part of our society. We not only have internet access at home and work, but people are on cell phones almost everywhere. The internet represents the absolute best and worst of humanity. You can discover so much about addiction recovery and so much about addiction in a very bad way.

Below, write out how the internet has been a part of your addictive behaviors.

I highly recommend getting accountability software on all of your computers and your cell phones. If you don't have this already, go to drdougweiss.com and you can download one today. For all my Christian friends, I definitely recommend you get the porn filter as well. Below I want you to list who will be receiving the accountability reports so someone knows where you are going on the Internet.

Name

1. _____

2. _____

3. _____

4. _____

5. _____

#21
Boundaries: Social Network

Today's addict faces an even more dangerous world. In the old days you had to go into the dealers part of the neighborhood, the part of town where they sold porn, or your neighborhood bar. Today, with social networks, the invitation to act out come to you on your phone and computer.

You don't need these social networks in your life. I have heard of addict after addict falling to an invitation from someone from the distant past, present or even a perfect stranger. You don't need to relapse here. You deserve to stay free your entire life. Here are some boundary selections for you to choose from about social networks.

1. No social networks

2. My spouse is on our page together and manages the site.

3. My sponsor/accountability person has full access including passwords

4. I make calls before and after being on these sites and be honest about the conversations.

#22
Opposite Sex Boundaries

Countless addicts have lost their sobriety through someone of the opposite sex. Someone from the opposite sex can be dangerous especially if he or she was a part of your addiction or you had a romantic or sexual relationship with them.

Single Christians need very clear sexual boundaries around physical touch regardless if they are 18 or 80 years old. Remember, self will is what got you and can keep you sick. Married people need boundaries around talking badly about their spouse, emotionally supporting the opposite sex (even in recovery), texting and physical contact. Below, write out your boundaries.

Single

1. During dating I will be accountable to _____ how often _____

2. My time frame for kissing the opposite sex is: _____

3. The latest I will be with the opposite sex is: _____

4. If I break my Opposite Sex Boundary, my consequence is: _____

Married

1. My texting/email boundaries are: _____

2. My consequence for talking poorly about my spouse to the opposite sex is : _____

3. My boundaries for physical contact with the opposite sex is: _____

4. I will be accountable to _____ for these behaviors.

#23
Listing My Boundaries

Compiling a single list of all your boundaries can help you be aware of the different facets of your addiction. This list of boundaries may be a helpful reminder to review daily or regularly during your recovery. Your boundaries are already written out on previous pages. Just place in the spaces below a concise list of all of these boundaries.

Boundaries for where I can go

_____   _____

_____   _____

_____   _____

Boundaries for who I can see

_____   _____

_____   _____

_____   _____

Boundaries for the internet

_____   _____

_____   _____

_____   _____

Boundaries for magazines

_____   _____

_____   _____

_____   _____

Boundaries for television viewing

_____   _____

_____   _____

_____   _____

Boundaries for movies/DVDs

_____   _____

_____   _____

_____   _____

Boundaries for personal social network

_____   _____

_____   _____

_____   _____

Boundaries for opposite sex

_____   _____

_____   _____

_____   _____

#24

Boundaries About Boundaries

In your recovery, you will go through many different stages. In time, during your growth, you may consider moving your boundaries. If the timing is right, this can be a positive experience, or it can lead to a relapse and may be a premeditated step toward a trigger or acting out.

In general, it is good to have some boundaries about boundaries. When changing your boundaries to be less restrictive, you may want to include talking to your spouse, sponsor, pastor or therapist before you make a decision. Ask God about the change, and wait for a week or month after you decide to move a boundary before you actually do it. Together these boundaries about boundaries are helpful to prevent you from arbitrarily changing them.

As an addict, you may be more likely to make a change because of a particular "feeling" instead of what may be in your best interest. Your addiction is very crafty at manipulating you through your emotions, so it is best to have an external source you can consult with to safeguard your precious recovery, especially during the first year of recovery.

Before changing a boundary, I will contact the following people.

1. _____

2. _____

3. _____

4. _____

#25
Sexual Boundaries

By now, you are probably getting the sense recovery from addiction has something to do with identifying and maintaining boundaries. This is true of any recovery, whether it is alcohol, drugs, sex or food. During your recovery, you will need to address the sex act itself, and identify what is healthy for you and your spouse.

The sexual history you may have had with your spouse may be long and scarred by your addiction. I have worked with couples where the addict involved their spouse in unwanted sexual behaviors. These events were traumatic for them. If these situations have occurred in your past, it may be necessary for you to consider providing them with professional help, so they can return to a healthy sexual relationship.

Boundaries involving the sex act need to be agreed upon by both partners, not just you. For most addicts, the growth in your sexuality will seem awkward at first, but in the long run, it will increase the possibility of a great, mutually enjoyable sex life together. You and your spouse may use the following checklist. Anything not marked with a "yes" by both partners would constitute something you will not engage in during your sex act. Remember, no pressuring!

You may also want to watch the class on Sex and Recovery in the AASAT training course. This tape has very useful information about sex during recovery, which your spouse may prefer to hear from me, as opposed to the person who has hurt her.

Sexual Behavior	Myself		My Wife	
_____	Y	N	Y	N
_____	Y	N	Y	N
_____	Y	N	Y	N
_____	Y	N	Y	N
_____	Y	N	Y	N
_____	Y	N	Y	N
_____	Y	N	Y	N
_____	Y	N	Y	N

Our mutual boundaries are:

_____   _____

_____   _____

_____   _____

If I violate these boundaries, my consequences are:

1st time _____

2nd time _____

3rd time _____

I will make myself accountable to my:

☐ Therapist   ☐ Sponsor   ☐ Other (same sex)

#26
Sexual Boundaries For the Unmarried

The single or divorced addict has to reestablish boundaries around their sexual behavior with others during recovery. The first of these boundaries might be "Who will I have sex with?" This may seem strange, since in your acting-out days, you would rarely disqualify anyone from a sexual acting-out experience. In recovery, the addict has learned sex is not about "getting something," rather about "relationships." Some areas of concern, as to whom you will have sex with, are:

1. My ex-spouse
2. Past relationships or acting-out partners
3. Prostitutes
4. Someone I just met or someone I have know less than a preset length of time
5. Someone I have no commitment toward
6. Someone who is married to someone else
7. Someone no more than 5, or so, years younger than myself.
8. Pornography
9. Masturbation with fantasy or porn

"When should I have sex?" This is a question a few addicts have pondered during their acting-out days. This question is also part of the boundary list you must develop as a recovering addict. Since sex, for a Christian, is about a marriage, a boundary is important to establish. Biblically, sex outside of marriage is a sin and will hurt you. This boundary may be something you will want to discuss with your group or support person.

"Why am I having sex?" This is also a great recovering question to ask yourself <u>before</u> you have sex, rather than afterward. Is a marital relationship a commitment you are willing to make to this person? Sex is a form of commitment and has meaning. God also shares this concept and wants you to have sex with only the person you are married to.

These boundaries also need to include your sexual boundaries with yourself.

My sexual boundaries are:

#27
Cell Phone Boundaries

Cell phones are an amazing device that we all utilize daily. A couple of decades ago we didn't even have access to all of our acting out partners at the touch of a button. We couldn't Google a hit for a particular drug of choice nor could we get on our favorite social network and avoid building healthy real relationships.

I know some people, and I'll bet you do too, who are almost addicted to their cell phone. I want you to strongly consider, especially in early recovery, some boundaries you may need.

1. Block cell numbers of people that are not a good influence.
2. Let go to voice mail numbers you don't know.
3. Review your cell bill with your spouse or accountability person.
4. Disconnect the browser to the internet.
5. Have accountability software on the phone.
6. Block people that are not a good influence from your e-mail.
7. Change you cell number and e-mail.
8. Delete any questionable people from your cell.

List your cell phone boundaries below:

_____

_____

_____

_____

1. If I relapse once on the cell phone, I will _____

2. If I relapse twice on the cell phone, I will _____

3. If I relapse three times on the cell phone, I will _____

4. For my cell phone boundaries, the person I will be accountable to is _____

5. I will check in on this issue with the above person on a:

☐ Daily   ☐ Weekly Basis

#28
Rerouting

Many addicts have particular driving routes, which feed their addiction. These routes may include driving by a certain convenience store, adult bookstore, liquor store or old flame's house. Many of these places become a regular part of the addict's driving route. Before or after work, or maybe on lunch break, the addict will go to one of several places to get a "look" to experience their addiction once again.

Conditioning yourself to these places is very powerful. Driving by any of the above places can often trigger you into thoughts of acting out or even rationalizations, such as "I've had a bad day. I deserve this." By simply driving by a place, many addicts can feel a rush. Some addicts even have to change their route to work because past places they participated in their addiction.

To reroute your driving, one must carefully consider the path you go to or from a geographical area. If you have a relapse because of your driving route, it definitely is an indication rerouting has to take place. For your personal recovery, you can make rerouting a part of your accountability check-in, so you will not drive by the possible relapse locations. Rerouting can help stop some of the ritual acting out, driving by an old familiar place where you have acted out so many times in the past.

If you feel you need to reroute to avoid a certain trigger write the areas you need to avoid and your alternate route.

1. _____

2. _____

3. _____

4. _____

5. _____

#29

Defensive Driving

As a general rule, addicts have the ability to disconnect from themselves, especially while driving. Clinicians use another word for disconnecting, called "disassociating" from oneself. Right before the addict goes into fantasy, they disassociates from themselves.

Driving is very conducive to achieving a disconnected or disassociated state. This is probably because of the routine of driving. The limited amount of concentration needed to drive, as well as the sheer repetition, demands little from your brain, so you can think about other things.

This is where the addict can start planting the seeds for their next "adventure." The addict needs a plan to drive defensively. Some driving tips other addicts found successful are listed below.

1. Utilize the rubber band technique while driving.

2. Listen to Christian-pop music or worship music.

3. Listen to talk radio instead of music. This engages your thoughts more than a song that you may have heard hundreds of times. You are also less likely to hear a song that may remind you of some event or person.

4. Listen to books on tape or recovery CDs.

5. Listen to scripture on CD I personally do this, it's good for your spirit.

6. Listen to sermons on CD.

7. Load your phone with things you like to listen to.

8. Make recovery phone calls if legal in your state to be on your phone in the car.

Practicing these tips may help your driving experience be less of a threat to your journey toward recovery. Driving defensively can keep you from beginning your addictive thoughts, which can lead to a more successful recovery, not to mention a safer drive!

#30
Accountability: Time

Addicts who want to act out have to find time to do so. This time they find may be used to just tease themselves or actually relapse. Since an addict has a secret life and does not tell anyone what behaviors they are up to, they have to develop a few escape patterns.

The first pattern is to lie about where they were and what they were doing. The second pattern that the addict develops is a lifestyle, including their job, which has wide open gaps of unaccountable time. Some favorite vocations for addicts appear to be salespeople of all types, doctors, lawyers, self-employed and other mobile jobs, which keep them unaccountable and unavailable for their time. This lifestyle makes it much easier for them to "slip out," so they can act out without anyone questioning them. The addict doesn't even have to lie directly. This is not to say those who have 9-to-5 jobs or those who stay in one location are less likely to be an addict. Addicts who have 9-to-5 jobs may develop "hobbies" or "social outlets," such as softball, which can leave blank spaces of time, so they can be unaccountable for their acting-out activities.

The point is acting out takes unaccountable time, so the reverse is true about getting into recovery. Achieving recovery for an addict means to be accountable with your time with someone of the same sex. This would exclude your spouse but may be your sponsor, someone else in the program or a friend who is aware of your situation and will go over your schedule with you. This will help you not feel, "Oh, I'm alone and nobody knows," which is very familiar to addicts and dangerous to a recovering addict. I'm not opposed to your spouse being a part of knowing, but someone of the same gender will be more objective with you and honestly less likely to believe you if things don't add up.

I will be accountable with my time to: _____

#31
Accountability: Money

Being accountable for finances has saved many addicts from acting out and losing their precious recovery. This technique can stop many forms of acting out instantly. For many addicts, most acting-out behaviors require money. Money is what makes the very sick world go around. Without money, even in the addict's most desperate emotional state, they cannot purchase anything. Simply put, accountability with money can save your sobriety.

How this can be practiced will probably be an individual matter. The following are some methods for financial accountability, which have helped some addicts in their recovery.

1. Strictly use credit card spending only and review statements with your wife or support person at the end of the month.

2. Cancel ATM card or have them alert your spouse or support person if you take a withdrawal.

3. Use checks only and review them monthly with support person.

4. Allow your spouse to be fully involved and aware of all finances.

5. Allow your spouse or support person to be fully aware of any secret stashes of money, odd jobs or freelance work you do and how much you earn.

Once you are committed to the concept of being financially accountable, and realize how it may be in your best interest for the first 6 to 12 months of your recovery, you will find a way to make money accountability work for you. When the creativity of an addict is working on how to make their recovery a priority, I find there is a lot of hope for their recovery. The addict who makes excuses and looks for ways they cannot be financially accountable is probably going to experience relapses, which involve money in their acting-out behaviors. This can be prevented by financial accountability.

Remember, addiction recovery is probably going to be the hardest undertaking of your life. You must be willing to go to any length. For most, this may initially require becoming financially accountable to someone. This technique can get to the bare roots of your acting out. My hope is those reading this exercise can take this step into a life of recovery from addiction.

I will be accountable to my finances to _____

#32
Step One

"We admitted that we were powerless over our addiction
and that our lives had become unmanageable"

This is the most important step of all. In Step One, you place your feet on the path toward recovery. "We" means you will have others involved with you in your recovery. Recovery is a team participation sport. "We admitted" is not all of Step One. Some people attend meetings and never complete Step One. Some simply admit they are an addict much like the alcoholic admits they are an alcoholic while drinking a beer.

Step One has us admit we are "powerless." Powerlessness is different than being addicted. Being addicted to cocaine could mean if you saw some cocaine, "you couldn't help yourself," and you would use the cocaine. Powerlessness would be if you saw the cocaine, you would run out, call someone and try any helpful behaviors to avoid what once controlled your life.

Many lives are tainted with the unmanageability addiction brings. In your recovery, sanity and order will replace the "crazies" and the chaos. Step One is the beginning to a lifestyle of recovery from addiction. In the workbook, Steps to Recovery, I provide over 20 pages that allow you to explore and experience Step One. This is how important I feel Step One is.

Behaviors that support Step One are:

Behavior	Yes	No
1. Prayer	_____	_____
2. Reading	_____	_____
3. Phone calls	_____	_____
4. Meetings	_____	_____
5. Staying accountable with your time and money	_____	_____
6. Creativity in your recovery	_____	_____

The day I completed my First Step was _____

#33
Ninety Meetings In Ninety Days

"Ninety meetings in ninety days" is an old Alcoholics Anonymous saying. It meant an alcoholic starting recovery was asked to attend an AA meeting every day. This behavior provided several benefits. It allowed the alcoholic to see recovery in the lives of others and gave hope for recovery. It enabled the alcoholic to hear what it meant to be honest about life. It gave the alcoholic a new group of people to call friends, and helped the addict receive support for struggles and gain recognition for efforts made to stay clean.

This tool works. Attending that many meetings up front will guarantee a change in your life. Unfortunately, only in very large cities would there be a possibility of this many meetings held for various addiction anonymous groups. The principle is true. Wherever you live, find the local Recovery Groups. Attend as many groups as possible for the first 90 days. It can help build the relationships you need to become and stay free.

Addiction recovery is a team sport. You <u>cannot</u> do it by yourself. The group will help you become successful in your recovery. Again, if you feel like starting a Recovery Group, a Christ-based, 12-Step support group, talk to your pastor. According to one of our studies of pastors across seven denominations with 14 years in the ministry, 84% stated they would welcome such a group in their church if a church member approached them and was willing to lead the group.

#34
Using Check-In Times

The 12-Step support groups vary in names and practices. To make it even more complicated, these groups vary from state to state.

Check-in time is something common in most 12-Step meetings. The check-in time is usually held at the beginning or end of the support group meeting. Larger groups, who wish to utilize check-in times, break off into smaller groups of two or three people. This is where you get "current" or honest about where you are for that particular day.

If there have been addiction fantasies or behaviors you have been involved in with your addiction, the check-in time is where you would be honest about it. Check-ins has saved many addicts from acting-out behaviors. This level of honesty can only keep you closer to your goal of recovery. If your group does not employ a check in-time, you can start this with one other person, so you can gain the benefit of this exercise.

In the early part of your recovery, make sure you check-in at every meeting you attend. This will save you some struggles with your addiction and make your recovery go much smoother. This will also keep you from getting lulled into a false sense of recovery by "just attending meetings." If all you do is attend meetings and are not using this time for personal honesty, you will struggle much more in your attempt to gain recovery. Remember, maximized thinking. Give as much of yourself as you can during check-ins, and you will not regret it.

#35
My Sponsor

A sponsor in a 12-step group is similar to a mentor or discipleship relationship. The sponsor can be someone who has been where you are and knows how to get further in recovery than you. A good sponsor would be someone you could call regularly and talk about recovery. A sponsor will encourage you to do your step work and help hold you accountable to goals you have set for yourself in recovery.

In picking a sponsor, you probably want to listen to others in your support group who are really in recovery. This would probably be someone who isn't reporting the latest relapse story, rather working the steps. It is best if this person has finished their fifth step. This eliminates your sponsor from helping you through your steps while dealing with their own garbage. After the fifth step, there is a lot less shame, and someone can be much healthier to help you.

Some addicts like to have a sponsor who has at least six months in the program or six months of recovery from bottom-line behaviors. This would be ideal.

Utilizing a sponsor relationship can help tremendously, so you do not feel alone during your recovery. This healthy relationship, hopefully, will allow you to see there is more in recovery for you in the future. Ask the person you are considering to be your sponsor when would be a good time to talk together about sponsorship. If you mutually agree, this would be your sponsor.

#36
Identifying And Communicating Feelings

Most addicts have difficulty with identifying feelings. If an addict, of any kind, has a feeling, he or she generally fixes it by taking a drink, using a drug, sex or some other way of medicating this feeling.

Most addicts have not had any experience from their family of origin in the area of how to have and share feelings. Feelings are a skill you can develop and acquire levels of mastery once you have practiced. This can be related to growing up and not learning how to maintain a car. It doesn't mean you are less intelligent or worthwhile because you cannot fix a car. You would be simply untrained. If you were to take a class on car maintenance, you would probably be a good mechanic. The difference is the skills you were exposed to and have learned will make you more skilled.

In addiction recovery, expressing feelings is very important for several reasons. Some are mentioned below.

1. If you had a feeling in your acting-out days, you probably would not know what it was. If you acted out in some way, the feeling would go away. In this process, you may not have learned to identify feelings and, hence, cannot meet your own real needs.

2. In your early recovery, usually between the third to sixth week of abstinence from your acting out behaviors you may begin to start recognizing feelings. These feels almost like a thawing out of emotions. It is best to have already begun to identify your feelings, so they don't confuse or overwhelm you and activate the cycle (feel -> act out-> feeling disappears). In recovery, you can now feel without acting out.

3. If you can identify your feelings, you may better know how to handle or manage these feelings in order to prevent relapses.

4. If a cycle or relapse occurs, you may be able to track down what emotion(s) preceded this and move forward in your recovery process.

5. Mastering your feelings can allow more intimacy into your life, and yes, it will make your relationships better too.

In the first month or so of your recovery, the feelings identification exercise may be one of the more difficult exercises in this book. The discipline you put into this exercise will have lifelong benefits in every area of your life, including relationships, parenting, work, recovery, spirituality and your social life. It may also save you from financial mistakes, because your intuition will become more active in your decision-making process.

The feelings exercise is simple. Fill in the blanks. An example is given below.

1. I feel (feeling word) when _____(Present tense)

2. I first remember feeling (same feeling word) when _____(Past tense)

Example:

1. I feel calm when I am on the lake in a boat with a friend.

2. I first remember feeling calm when I was 10 years old. I had my own bedroom where I played with a race car set.

The goal here is to have two experiences. In computer terms, an addict has an emotional database, but this database has no file names, so you cannot access the files, nor can you utilize this data. If you do this exercise two or more times daily for three months, it will make your journey toward recovery a lot smoother. Those who do this in their recovery early never regret it later. Those who do not do this exercise always regret it. I strongly encourage you to take the time to do this exercise today and for the next several weeks.

A feelings list you can utilize for your feeling exercises is located in the Appendix of this book. The list is in alphabetical order. You can select any feeling from the feelings list you wish to randomly practice sharing your feelings exercise.

Feelings Communication

When you have ten or more of your feelings identified, it is important you begin to communicate them to a safe person. A safe person may be someone in your recovery group or a person who you are accountable to. The person's role is simply to listen, not really provide feedback, which can be helpful. If you choose your spouse, make sure this is safe for you, and make sure your examples do not involve your spouse in any way.

If you involve your spouse, they can do the exercise to identify and communicate feelings back to you also. This can be a great opportunity to develop intimacy. If these experiences turn into disagreements, the exercise is being done incorrectly, and you may need to pick another person or a therapist to do them with.

When sharing your feelings, it is important to maintain eye contact with the person you are sharing them with. Eye contact with this person may feel uncomfortable at first but eventually will be comfortable to you. This is part of the benefit of this exercise. If you do them with your spouse, there is to be no discussion of what was shared in this exercise until 72 hours after the feeling was shared.

#37
Dangerous "E" Zones

Emotions for addicts can be tricky. Early in recovery, many addicts have few feeling skills. During your recovery, especially after completing your feeling exercises, you will become better acquainted with yourself and your feelings.

Being aware of your feelings will be helpful, but it will not make them less difficult. In your recovery journey, you will find some feelings are very difficult for you to manage. Some feelings may include, but are not limited to, feeling bored, lonely, angry, hopeless, worthless, shame and rejection.

These difficult feelings are what I call the dangerous "E" zones. They are feelings you have skillfully avoided or medicated during your addiction. Often these feelings are what you received from your addiction in reverse, such as active, connected, content, hopeful, esteemed, shameless and fully accepted. This is what makes these feelings a possible dangerous "E" zone. They represent a cluster of feelings you rarely felt without your addiction.

During your recovery, you need to discover your dangerous "E" zones. The easiest way is to review the feelings list, and place a mark by the feelings you believe to be most difficult for you.

List these feeling words below.

_____   _____

_____   _____

_____   _____

_____   _____

_____   _____

#38
Action Plan For My Feelings

In the previous exercise, you listed the feelings that could be your dangerous "E" zones. In this exercise, you will take the time to give yourself several options if you get into one of these zones. Having a written plan ahead of time helps a lot in recovery. This exercise will be a greater help if you can practice and hold the feeling for 15 seconds. Then, implement a plan of your choice. This practice will help when the real battle is on.

The following is an example to practice.

I feel <u>bored</u>.   Hold this <u>bored</u> feeling 15 to 30 seconds. Call someone in the program.

Below list the feelings that are dangerous "E" zones for you, and list three behavioral options for that feeling.

Example:

Feeling: Bored

1. Call someone

2. Go to a meeting

3. Exercise

Feeling: _____

1. _____

2. _____

3. _____

Feeling: _____

1. _____

2. _____

3. _____

Feeling: _____

1. _____

2. _____

3. _____

#39
Avoid H.A.L.T

During the recovery process, whether it is for alcohol, drugs, sex or food, H.A.L.T. has been used in support group settings to stand for Hungry, Angry, Lonely and Tired. These are important things to avoid for the all recovering addicts. Simply put, keep yourself eating regularly and properly. Do not allow yourself to get too hungry, which may make your more susceptible to less logical thinking. Some researchers believe eating certain foods can help you in recovery. A book that addresses this aspect of recovery is Help Yourself, by Joel Robertson and published by Thomas Nelson Publishing.

Anger can sneak up on you quickly and put you in an emotional state of "I'll show you." You could begin to rationalize why it might be okay to act out. Some addicts have a whole system where they purposely start a fight with their spouse, leave, act out and come back later, justifying their acting-out behavior, because they were "Angry." Anger can be an important piece of managing your recovery.

Lonely is a difficult feeling for the addict to handle. Feeling alone can make the addict vulnerable and create a desire to medicate by acting out. When you get lonely, it may be helpful to have an action plan or an "I-will-do" list available in your wallet. Some other suggestions are listed below.

1. Go to a public place, such as a mall, restaurant, etc.

2. Call someone in the program.

3. Plan ahead to avoid your alone time gaps, such as weekends or when your wife may be out of town.

4. Exercise.

5. Help someone else with a project.

6. Go to a meeting, church or other social gathering.

7. Pray.

8. Ask others what they do.

Being "Tired" in your busy, fast paced life is a familiar feeling. Tiredness can lower your resistance to the point of "who cares." To recover, we need to stay alert. Our addiction is a default program that desires to be fully activated anytime it can find an outlet. To prevent tiredness, get regular sleep. If you need to rest here or there, do so if possible.

List your action plan for the following:

Hungry _____

Angry _____

Lonely _____

Tired _____

#40
My Worst Moment

In the addict's active, addicted lifestyle, they rarely think of the pain they are causing themselves or anyone else. In recovery from addiction, when the addiction "talks to you," it will try to sell you as it says, "A little bit won't hurt" or "Who will know?" "You can act out just one more time." "You are sober enough." "It won't affect your recovery." These and many other lies try to maximize the current benefit your addiction will give to you (i.e. it feels good) and minimize the long-term effects (i.e. this could be the beginning of 2-to-10-year binge. You could lose your marriage, business). This addiction is very crafty!

A tool that has helped recovering addicts maintain recovery is having a negative experience locked in, almost memorized, which maximizes the pain and minimizes the pleasure to act out. For some addicts, this picture could include the possibility of getting caught by the police. For others, their worst picture is getting kicked out of the house for good, seeing their children's faces when they leave, seeing their spouse cry, hearing a judge say "no visitation privileges," the loss of a job, risking AIDS or even abortions. These are only a few experiences. You may have one or more painful moments. You may want to write down these experiences to remind yourself.

After you write down these experiences, picture it in your mind, as vividly as you can, and feel the feelings. Practice this picture in a public place, where you are not as likely to act out, 2 to 3 times a day for three days. Rehearsing this image and feeling will make you ready to beat the addiction when it starts talking to you.

My three painful experiences were:

1. _____

2. _____

3. _____

Days I practiced this exercise

_____   _____

_____   _____

_____   _____

#41
What My Addiction Cost Me

Every addiction costs the addict something. You can talk about emotional, relational, social and vocational losses that occurred due to your addiction all day. Although these are all important, there is a practical side to the addict. The cost, in financial terms, has helped some addicts once again put in perspective the damage their addiction has done to their life.

The knowledge of estimated financial damage has helped some addicts say "no" to acting out. When clients have done this exercise in my office, the average cost over the lifetime of the addict to the point they began recovery was approximately $250,000 dollars. Most of us wish we had that amount on hand today. To list the cost of your addiction, you may want to consider several things:

Time value of your addiction (See Appendix) _____

Cost of actual material purchased _____

Cost of professional services to recover _____

Cost of legal fees (including divorce) _____

Divorce losses _____

Child support _____

Missed opportunities (college, job promotions) _____

Working in a job below your abilities _____

Loss of creativity and energy over the years _____

Guilt spending (to make you or your spouse feel better) _____

Geographical moves (running from addiction) _____

Emotional/financial immature choices due to addiction _____

Other _____ _____

Other _____ _____

Other _____ _____

Total $_____

In other exercises in this book, such as What My Addiction Took from Me, What My Addiction Cost Me and My Worst Moment, you may have discovered in several dimensions what you addiction has really cost you. This realization can be truly painful, and you can have very sad feelings accompanying this realization.

Although, at the moment you do feel this pain and discomfort, there will also be days ahead when your addiction will attempt to have you forget this moment. If your addiction can make you forget this pain and discomfort, it will be easier to talk you into "another ride" on the addiction train. It is in this pain and discomfort, feeling what your addiction has cost you, that will keep you from doing it again. In the hopes of strengthening your recovery and giving you one more tool to recover by, you can capture this moment of pain to rescue yourself in the future days when your addiction wants you to join in again and destroy you.

Use the back of a blank business card, and write at the top the word "COST" along with what your addiction has cost you and what it could cost you five years from now. Write yourself some notes only you would understand, and place it in your billfold or purse. When you start to feel the addiction talk you into acting out, pull out your card and talk back. Having the facts places truth on your side, and you may escape a relapse this time. You can also just put this cost information in your cell phone as well to be really helpful.

Example:

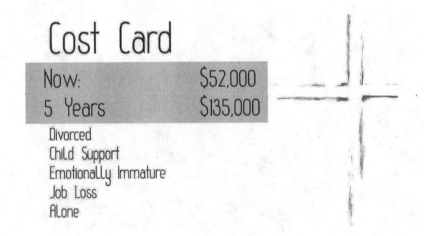

Cost Card

Now:	$52,000
5 Years	$135,000

Divorced
Child Support
Emotionally Immature
Job Loss
Alone

#43
Reward Card

The reward card is very similar to the cost card. Actually, it is the reverse of the cost card. On the backside of a business card or in your phone, place some of the rewards you see for yourself if you maintain a successful recovery from your addiction, such as your family and job. Be as specific as possible in your rewards, such as staying married, seeing my children grow up, probably making more money and better relationships.

Place these rewards on the backside of this business card, so you can clearly understand it at a quick glance. Some have found it helpful to tape the two cards together with rewards and cost easily read so in the "heat of the battle" with your addiction, you have both the pain of the past and the hope of the future to fight back. This two-edged sword can help you win one battle at a time.

If this tool helps you win the battle of addiction just one time, it is worth keeping in your phone, wallet or purse for at least the first year of your recovery from addiction.

My rewards are:

_____

_____

_____

_____

_____

_____

#44
Calling Card

In recovery, as we discussed earlier, a phone call may be your only link to reality. In a moment, the addiction can sweep you off your feet and have you swirling in thoughts, pictures, devices and an entire host of feelings. It is as if you fell off a boat, and it is moving away, leaving you in a storm. Somehow you need to connect to the boat, so someone, anyone, can throw you a life preserver to save you.

In the case of the addiction storm, you can pull out your phone card, call someone and recover safely to the shore from the waters of your addiction. If you were left to yourself, you may have drowned this time.

Simply put, keep phone numbers in your wallet, car, cell phone, home and your office. When you feel the storm coming or while it may be in full swing, you will be able to call someone at any place and anytime, so you don't have to experience a relapse that day. Remember, you don't recover by yourself. It is much better to call first than to relapse and have to call later. The calling card is one tool that can save you in a difficult situation, so make your card as soon as possible.

Recovery Numbers in My Cell Phone:

1 _____   5 _____
2 _____   6 _____
3 _____   7 _____
4 _____   8 _____

The day I made my calling card: _____

Recovery for Everyone Workbook   61

#45
The Other Problem

Working with addicts for more than twenty years I have discovered another problem addicts tend to have. This problem only shows up in their marriage, although it can also be with an addict who only has short term relationships for decades.

The problem is intimacy anorexia. Intimacy anorexia is the active withholding of spiritual, emotional and sexual intimacy from the spouse. The spouse will complain of feeling like a roommate. The characteristics are below. Answer these questions as your spouse would answer these question or even better, have them answer these questions.

1. I stay so busy that I have little time for my spouse.
2. When issues come up my first reflex or response is to blame my spouse.
3. I withhold love from my spouse.
4. I withhold praise from my spouse.
5. I withhold sex from my spouse or are not present during sex.
6. I withhold spiritual connection from my spouse.
7. I am unwilling or unable to share my authentic feelings with my spouse.
8. I use anger or silence to control my spouse.
9. I have ongoing or ungrounded criticism (spoken or unspoken) towards my spouse.
10. I control or shame my spouse regarding money or spending.

#46
Relapse And Research

If you scored 5 or above you might want to get more information on intimacy anorexia at intimacyanorexia. com. If this is unaddressed in your recovery it can lead to cyclical relapses due to the pain you are causing intentionally in your marriage. Relapses in the very beginning may occur. Turning a relapse into research is very important to prevent you from making the exact same mistake again. Researching your relapse takes rigorous honesty.

If you relapse, ask yourself the following questions.

1. What were my feelings prior to acting-out?

2. What red flags did I pass up?

3. What tools in my recovery did I choose not to use?

4. How many days have I been planning this event?

5. Relapsing takes time, energy and sometimes money. What was the significance or importance to this acting-out event?

6. At what point did I begin to feel "powerful" over my addiction?

7. Have I regularly kept the Five Commandments prior to acting-out?

8. What have I learned about myself in this relapse?

9. What have I learned about my addiction?

10. What needs to be different so I don't relapse this way again?

11. Do I have to change some boundaries to stay free from addiction?

The date I shared this with my support person: _____

The date I shared this with my support group: _____

#47
Travel Tips

In today's world, it is not uncommon to go on business trips out of town or even out of the state or country. For some addicts, this was their prime acting-out time. Unaccountable time and money make a dangerous combination for your addiction that desires to flare up, even in your recovery.

The following are traveling tips, which have been used by those who have been successful in their addiction recovery.

1. If you travel a lot, go online in advance to find available meetings at the location you are traveling.

2. Call the contact listed for the addiction meeting in the city you are visiting, and make a break fast, lunch or dinner appointment, so you know you'll be talking recovery with someone of the same gender while on your trip.

3. Call your hotel before you leave to cancel all adult channels, alcohol in the bar and/or pay-per-view television. (If you ask them, they will remove the television from your room also) or anything that could impact your particular addiction.

4. Take two rubber bands with you: one to put on your wrist to keep you from fantasy on your addiction and the second to place around the armoire door knobs, which contain the television to keep you from watching it "unintentionally."

5. Schedule at least daily phone calls to people in your home group before you leave.

6. Take at least one addiction recovery book or workbook. Steps to Recovery or this book would be great choices.

7. When lonely, go to a public area in the hotel, never the bar.

8. Keep the Five Commandments as much as possible while traveling.

9. Block all porn and social networking on your computer or use the Internet in the business center only.

Part2
Personal Growth Recovery Techniques

Step Two

"Came to believe a power greater than ourselves could restore us to sanity."

Coming to believe in one power that is able to heal you is a process. As Christians, we know this power is Jesus Christ. So did the writer of the Twelve Steps. The first writing of the Twelve Steps used the word "God" in place of "power greater than ourselves." In the 1930's, they didn't think our culture would broaden this to anything else. In current traditional Twelve-Step groups (not Recovery Groups), they take this step to loosely, but in Step Three, they continue with the word "God." Remember, believing is behaving. "If you love me, you will keep my commandments" (John 14:15.) Some addicts have so much shame about what they have done and who they have hurt, they may feel defective.

In Step Two, if you have a religious background, this may be a place for you to rediscover a forgotten heritage. For others, you will start with a totally clean slate spiritually and receive the joy of discovering for the first time a connection with Jesus Christ. A more thorough exploration of Step Two is given in the Steps to Recovery workbook made available as an e-book located at drdougweiss.com.

Behaviors that support Step Two are:

Behavior	Yes	No
1. Honesty about your spiritual place	_____	_____
2. Prayer	_____	_____
3. Meditation	_____	_____
4. Biblical reading	_____	_____
5. Dialoguing with others, whom you feel have a good relationship with Jesus.	_____	_____

The day I completed my Second Step was _____

#49
What My Addiction Gave Me

When you think about a relationship as long as you have had with your addiction, which may be 10, 20, 30 or more years, you have had quite a relationship. You ran to your addiction to celebrate, be encouraged and feel wanted, powerful, in control and confident and on a regular basis. For most addicts, their addiction was the only committed relationship they kept over the years.

Your addiction has given many things to you, including a false world, kept your secret(s), false intimacy, a sense of success, acceptance, a completely unconditional loving relationship regardless of your deviancy, and the list goes on. In thinking about this, you must realize you received a lot from your addiction. If you didn't, you would have stopped a long time ago. In light of this, each of you received different things out of your relationship with your addiction. It is important in your recovery you know what it was you received from your addiction.

Make a real, honest effort to list as many things you can that you have received from your addiction. You can probably come up with 20 things your addiction gave to you.

1. _____
2. _____
3. _____
4. _____
5. _____
6. _____
7. _____
8. _____
9. _____
10. _____

11. _____
12. _____
13. _____
14. _____
15. _____
16. _____
17. _____
18. _____
19. _____
20. _____

#50
Thank You Letter

As you completed the previous exercise, listing the good things your addiction has done for you, the realization of how powerful, intimate and dynamic your relationship was with your addiction is obvious. Write a thank you letter to your addiction for all the things it has done for you. This will further crystallize in a false sense how, through the relationship with your addiction, you were getting your needs met and had many years of devoted, although ultimately destructive, service toward you. You may need to use an additional piece of paper for this exercise.

To My Addiction,

_____

_____

_____

_____

_____

_____

_____

_____

_____

_____

_____

_____

_____

_____

#51
What My Addiction Took From Me

For every relationship, you can create a list of losses and gains from it. Within an addictive relationship, the list of what this relationship took from me is usually equal to or greater than the list of what the relationship temporarily gave to me. Nowhere does this have more truth than with addiction.

My addictions have stolen many years of my life and emotions. It had taken my ability to communicate due to the shame, guilt and fear of being exposed. I felt isolated and less than. I was scared about my secrets and feared never being truly loved. I was glassed in and couldn't feel a way out. I had a sense I was going nowhere. The list could go on and on, such as "Will I ever be normal again?" or "Can God still love me?" We each have our own list of what the addiction has taken from us. It is important in your recovery to look at these losses honestly. In the following spaces, list your losses your addiction has caused.

1. _____

2. _____

3. _____

4. _____

5. _____

6. _____

7. _____

8. _____

9. _____

10. _____

11. _____

12. _____

13. _____

14. _____

15. _____

16. _____

17. _____

18. _____

19. _____

20. _____

21. _____

22. _____

23. _____

24. _____

25. _____

26. _____

27. _____

28. _____

29. _____

30. _____

#52
Goodbye Letter

There is a time of reckoning for every bad relationship, a time when you have to confront the relationship, and say, "this is not working for me." Many have had to do this with several unhealthy relationships. Some have had to go through the divorce process.

It is now that time for your relationship with your addiction. You can see by your list of what has been taken from you that you can no longer continue in such a harmful relationship. You must confront your addiction face to face, so to speak, and say goodbye to it. Your addiction isn't worth the past damage or the guaranteed progressive damage it can cause. There is a saying: "a mind is a terrible thing to waste," and in the addict's case, it is your soul that is a terrible thing to waste.

During this sobering moment in your life, no matter how difficult, you must say goodbye to your relationship with your addiction. In the space below, write a goodbye letter to your addiction.

Dear Addiction,

_____

_____

_____

_____

_____

_____

_____

_____

_____

_____

#53
Empty Chair

The "empty chair" exercise has helped many clients in therapy, not only experience but also further the work they have completed in the previous exercises. The deeper you confront your addiction, the better sense of resolve you will experience, which may be the one tool that may help you stay clean for the day.

In this exercise, you will sit in a chair. Place another empty chair directly in front of you. While sitting in the chair, be sure to have your thank you and goodbye letters you wrote to your addiction with you. Read your letters out loud, as if the addiction was a real person sitting in the chair in front of you. No one else needs to be there unless you want support from a therapist. For most of your life, the addiction was a real person. Addicts' experiences with this exercise have varied. In the space below, you can list your thoughts and feelings regarding this exercise.

My thoughts are: _____

_____

_____

My feelings are: _____

_____

_____

The date I completed this exercise: _____

#54
Grief Stages

The addiction you have has probably been your best friend and may seem like your only true friend. Quite possibly, it has been there faithfully since adolescence. It has nurtured you, told you that you were special and worthwhile. It has accepted you no matter what hurts you brought or what kind of mood you were in that day. Choosing recovery is to divorce yourself from this almost daily relationship, which may know more about you than anyone else.

When you truly divorce yourself from your addiction, you will go through a grieving process. This process is normal and healthy. This exercise is to help expose you to the stages of grief, so you can understand and identify which stage you find yourself in and discover the future stages ahead of you.

Shock - This is the moment you realized you really were an addict. Numbness or a sense of emotional nausea may accompany this. This stage is usually fleeting but may last minutes, hours or sometimes days.

Denial - This stage can last for years. Some addicts in denial will say to their spouses, "I'm not the one with the problem, you are. It's normal to do this. This isn't sick. You are just naive." These statements, and a thousand other statements like them, are evidence of denial. Basically, if you are in denial, you "don't have a problem."

Anger - This is the first stage in which you begin to process that you "may" be an addict. You are probably very angry at this realization. "Why me?" "Why can't I act out in my own way? Other people can." You may dislike that you are an addict intensely, but at least you are finally wrestling with the painful truth of being an addict. This stage is often accompanied by irritability, mood swings and irrational behavior.

Bargaining - This is the stage someone might say, "I'm not an addict if..." The "if" can be "if I can stop for a while..." or "if I can just stop one aspect of my behavior." The addict may wish that "if my spouse or life was different, then I would not have this problem." Bargaining seeks to relieve the sting of the fact that you may be an addict. This is a very creative stage.

Sorrow - This is when it starts hitting you. You are an addict. This may not feel very good, but it is true. You know things need to change. You can feel it. You are sad about the fact of being an addict and maybe what it has done to your life and the lives of those you tried to love.

Acceptance - "I am an addict." You now accept responsibility for your addiction. You are no longer blaming or looking for a magical way to avoid the process of recovery. Your behavior is active in recovery. Your creativity is being used to find time and ways to recover, and you are being honest, even when it hurts.

In the space below, circle the stage you believe you are currently in. In a few weeks, check back and see if there is movement. Grief is a process. Being in grief is okay, because if you pass denial, you are actively going through the reality of being an addict. You can also write about each stage you have experienced.

Shock	Denial	Anger	Bargaining	Sorrow	Acceptance

Shock _____

_____

Denial _____

_____

Anger _____

_____

Bargaining _____

_____

Sorrow _____

_____

Acceptance _____

_____

#55
Meeting My Needs

After you have completed the feeling exercise for a while, you will have become more skilled at knowing what your feelings are. The skill of knowing your feelings is a necessary prerequisite to being able to meet your needs.

In your addiction in the past, if you had a feeling, you rarely knew what it was. If you acted out in some way, the feeling would go away, and you never knew what the real need was. Therefore, you couldn't be responsible to meet your real need. In order to maintain your recovery, you must not only become aware of your feelings and needs, you must take responsibility for them as well. Your spouse or others are not responsible if you feel alone, confused, overwhelmed or frustrated. You are responsible for your feelings and the needs those feelings create. You need to come up with alternatives to meet your needs in a healthy way.

Example:

In Addiction:

I don't know the feeling. > I act out. > The feeling goes away.

In Recovery:

I know the feeling. > creates a need. > I am aware and responsible to meet my need. > My need is met.

Action:

I feel alone. > I need to connect with someone. > I make phone call. > I'm no longer feeling alone.

On a separate piece of paper, write out examples of how you are currently doing this exercise well. Also, write the needs you are not managing well, and make a plan for these needs to be met. Since your addiction was medicating your true self, don't be surprised by your needs. You may have more needs in recovery than you had while you were medicating them in your addiction.

Date I wrote out my needs: _____

#56
My Spouse

Your spouse has probably suffered in many ways from your addiction, possibly including tolerating your inability to be emotionally intimate, accepting financial losses, humiliation and the list goes on. If your spouse has decided work through this with you as you recover, you are very fortunate.

"What should I tell my spouse?" is one of the first questions I hear from an addict who wants to protect their marriage. The answer is situational. I will offer the following possible options. You may need a therapy session to help you personally in this area.

Options

1. Tell your spouse everything.
2. Tell your spouse selective information.
3. Tell vaguely without details "I had an affair," "used drugs," "drank."
4. Never tell.

After you decide to tell or not to tell your spouse, another issue is how much you include your spouse in your recovery process. In most cases, your spouse will not be an addict and will not understand your addictive thinking or other behavioral struggles. Your spouse is not your sponsor. Your sponsor needs to be someone of the same sex. It is helpful for your spouse to be aware of where you are in your recovery. You may want to agree on some questions your spouse can ask you that you will answer honestly.

Below are some examples of the types of questions you may want to suggest that your spouse may ask on a weekly or biweekly, agreed-upon basis about your recovery.

1. Have you crossed your bottom line?
2. Have you flirted with your addiction in any manner?
3. How often are you going to meetings?
4. Review the five commandments: Prayer, reading, meetings, call and prayer.

In my experience with other addicts, it is a good idea to plan a weekly or biweekly meeting with your spouse to discuss these questions. This can prevent your spouse from coming up with questions at anytime or during an argument. If your spouse is staying with you during your recovery, it can be therapeutic and appropriate for you both in order to keep it in a manageable session. If you have specific questions about these issues, you may want to speak to a therapist.

#57
Step Three

"Made a decision to turn our life and will
over to the care of God as we understood Him"

Making a decision of this magnitude can and should take some time in your recovery process. In Step Two, we were spending time with God, discovering His existence and how this relationship is working out. Having a relationship with God is much like those who get married. First, we dated our spouse. Eventually, over time and experiences, we decided to marry them and followed through with this decision. The decision to marry affected every part of our life socially, financially, sexually and emotionally. In various other areas, marriage redefined us and our behaviors. Turning your life over to the care of God is a similar experience. It is walking down the aisle with God and a lifelong commitment to stay in a relationship. This relationship grows over time. The depth of our experience and time together will reinforce our conception of God. As a Christian struggling with addiction, turning your desires over to God will be essential. It will be very important to be willing to accept His interpretation of your needs and trust Him to meet them. A much more thorough discussion of Step Three is available in the Steps to Recovery workbook.

Behaviors that support Step Three are:

Behavior	Yes	No
1. Prayer	_____	_____
2. Spiritual reading	_____	_____
3. Asking God to be involved in every area of your life	_____	_____
4. Behaviorally follow what you know to be God's will, even when you want it another way	_____	_____

The day I completed my Third Step was _____

#58
Five Years From Now: Unrecovered

In the more sober moments of your recovery, it is helpful to reinforce how dangerous your addiction can be. When your addiction is luring you back into its unsuspecting web, it has a sneaky way of presenting only pretty pictures. Addiction will never tell you how bad it can be as an addict over a period of years. In your recovery, it is helpful to have a clear counter picture in your mind to fight your addiction. Imagine what it would be like five years from now in an active, addicted lifestyle without recovery where you are hurting yourself along with others. As a helpful tool against your addiction, include your feelings in this picture.

In the lines below or on a separate sheet of paper, write out what you think your life would be like if you didn't stay in recovery and went back to an active, addicted lifestyle. The following situations can be included in your picture.

1. People you would be hanging around
2. People you wouldn't be seeing (spouse/children)
3. Where you would be living
4. The condition of your marriage if married
5. Possibly your next spouse and what this person would be like
6. Your relationship with your children
7. Your health and risk of disease
8. Your job and the direction of your career
9. The amount of time and energy spent on your addiction
10. How you would feel about yourself
11. Your secrets
12. Your spiritual condition and any other situations you can think of to include

My life without recovery 5 years from now:

Practice imagining the picture with the emotions you have listed above. Your addiction has thousands of pictures with emotions to use against you. Practice this picture 2 to 3 times a day for 3 to 5 days, as a tool to help you get and stay clean.

#59
Picture Yourself: Unrecovered

In the space provided, draw a picture of yourself in light of five years without recovery.

Describe yourself:

_____

_____

_____

Describe your feelings:

_____

_____

_____

Commit this picture to memory along with the feelings you have about it. Practice this picture 2 to 3 times a day for 3 to 5 days. This experience can help you counter the "pretty" picture of your addiction.

#60
Five Years From Now: Recovering

Fighting your addiction with pictures is an effective way to help you combat the times your addiction wants to creep back in. Many times your addiction tries to sneak back in through pictures. Your addiction knows how your brain works, how powerful pictures are and that vivid, reinforced pictures are quickly accessible to the brain's memory.

With this in mind, some addicts can counter fight the addiction with painful pictures of their addiction and their bleak future with it. Another helpful picture to combat our addiction is the picture of the addict having a successful recovery, enjoying themselves, their marriage, family, career, other relationships and activities.

As someone who has experienced the positive picture of recovery and living a happy, fulfilling and balanced life, I know this picture helps fight off the addiction when it wants to sneak its ugly head in. In the space provided below or on a separate sheet of paper, write out what you think your life would be like if you maintain recovery from addiction, as well as growth in your life of recovery. The following situations could be included in your response.

1. The friends you would have
2. Your career
3. Your marital status
4. Your relationship with your children
5. Your health and risk of sexual diseases
6. How you feel about yourself
7. Secrets you would have
8. Your spiritual lifestyle
9. Recreational interests or hobbies
10. Anything else you see for yourself in a positive future of recovery

My Life in recovery 5 years from now:

Take this picture and practice it 2 to 3 times a day for 3 to 5 days along with the feelings that go with it. This picture can be yours. After the hard work that comes with a healthy recovery, there can be fulfillment in every area of your life, spiritual, emotional, health, marriage, friendship, family and financial. My hope is you experience this picture. I have experienced it, and I know you can too.

My feelings about this picture:

_____

_____

_____

_____

_____

_____

_____

#61
Picture Yourself: Recovering

In the space below, draw a picture of yourself after five years of successful recovery.

Describe yourself:

_____

_____

_____

_____

Describe your feelings:

_____

_____

_____

_____

Commit this picture to memory along with the feelings you have about it. This, among the other pictures you practice 2 to 3 times each day for 3 to 5 days, can provide another positively reinforced picture to help you remain in recovery.

#62
My Family and Addiction

As a researched phenomenon, we know addictions often run in families. During your recovery process, it may be beneficial to do what clinicians call a genogram, which is another name for a family tree.

This exercise can be made very complicated by listing divorces, etc. However, for our purposes, simply draw your family tree with your family's first names only. With a different colored pen, write any addiction that you feel this relative may have had next to their name. A possible list might be alcohol, drugs, sex, gambling, food, television, nicotine, work, shopping and so on. If you are aware of sexual abuse or sexual addiction in your family tree, place an asterisk next to that relative's name as well.

This exercise was developed to help you put your addiction in a family context. This helps you to see that you definitely didn't get where you are all by yourself. In some cases, this can highlight other possible addictions you may have to look at after a substantial sobriety from your current addiction.

#63
Addiction In My Family

The genogram in the last exercise brought to light those in your family with various addictions. In the spaces below, list the family members you feel have the same addiction issues and why. Secondly, list those who you think were sexually abused in your family tree and why. If you believe no one in your family has had either issue, you may be very fortunate, or you just may not have all the information (some families keep better secrets than others.)

Name/Relationship	Why
1. _____	_____
2. _____	_____
3. _____	_____
4. _____	_____
5. _____	_____
6. _____	_____

While specifically looking at your particular addiction, you can sometimes see how this addiction has been carried throughout family generations. In my family, sex addiction and sexual abuse are on both sides of my family tree. Those that were in recovery from Alcoholics Anonymous when it just started in the 1930s had this same realization. They knew the addiction was in the family, but the knowledge about the disease wasn't available. The support groups were not there, and there certainly was not a book like the one you are reading that could help them step by step to make recovery their choice. Many in your family history had few choices of recovery or healing from this addiction. Write down your thoughts and feelings about possibly being the first in your family to be able to choose this recovery.

_____

_____

_____

#64
My Sexual History

A sexual history is something that many addicts have stored in their minds. Periodically, faces, pictures and events may come into your mind. These pictures sometimes stir up feelings of all different kinds. You may be less than proud of your sexual history, but regardless of where you are in your recovery, your sexual history can be a tool to help you see and discover things about yourself and your addiction.

To write a sexual history, get a pen and paper and simply go through your life in increments of 5 years (for example, 1-5, 6-10, 11-15, 16-20...). Write down all your sexual experiences. This would include exposure to pornography at various ages, masturbation patterns and your first sexual experience. When done thoroughly, this history will help you when you complete your Fourth Step. The temptation will be to avoid complete honesty.

A complete history will have several benefits, such as:

1. It is finally all out.

2. Great progress toward your Fourth Step.

3. You will be able to do the Sex Cycles Exercise.

In the previous exercise, you took great courage to write out your sexual history. This is important and can help you identify patterns from your sexual experiences.

Some addicts review their sexual histories and find a series of re-victimizations, or their first sexual experience was abusive, and they were used as someone's object. Others find cycles of intensity under stress or right after a major abandonment. You may also discover something about those you chose to be sexual with, such as they were emotionally unavailable or unfaithful. Other sexual experiences might be victimizing others or the continual reliance on masturbation and/or pornography at the expense of relationships. A pattern of being unfulfilled sexually and seeking the magic fix can also emerge. For some, stress and financial pressure are related to sexual cycles. Others, when they have extra money, can see they exhibit a pattern of acting out. Some discover traveling out of town as a pattern. For some addicts, a definite binge-purge pattern emerges, where they are "good" for so long, and then they act out excessively. There are even some addicts who avoid sexuality with their spouse (Intimacy Anorexia). There is a myriad of possible sexual cycles. In the below space, briefly write out the cycles you recognize in your sexual history.

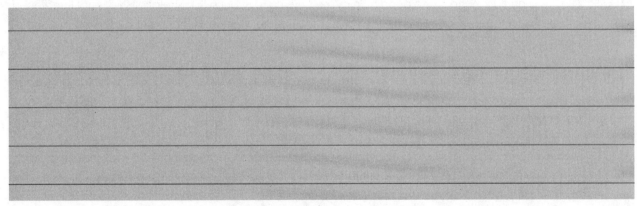

Now that you have identified some cycles, as they relate to your sexual history, you may for the first time realize the reality of certain cycles or patterns in your acting-out behaviors. To make the most of these realizations, it will help if you make a plan or strategy to "short circuit" the patterns that are already in place. Even those in marriages will have patterns in their marriage that can be healthy or unhealthy.

#66
Types of Sex

The types of sex listed below are excerpts taken from the book Partners: Healing from His Addiction. This approach can help you to identify the type of sex you have had with your spouse. The addict is often amazed that after 5 to 10 or more years of addiction that it actually can impact even their sex life. Many addicts and their spouses have rarely even had relational sex during their entire marriage.

The awareness of the types of sex can help you aim for relational sex in your recovery. It will also help you to be empathetic to the type of sex you have conditioned yourself and your spouse to participate in throughout your relationship. In recovery, you can have a growing sexual relationship that is not only relational but also nurturing and fulfilling as well.

Relational Sex: Both enjoy each other as a person and are able to communicate sexual needs to one another. One or both may or may not have an orgasm, but both have a sense of nurturing each other. Sex is not the focus or the priority in this relationship.

Physical Sex: This is primarily where one or both enjoy the physical act, but still, the relationship is not threatened. This type of sex may happen at one time or another to all couples. There may not be much feeling, but shame is not a factor.

Objectifying Sex: This type of sex may or may not be pleasurable for the wife. The addict is fantasizing about other sexual acts with his wife. One person's orgasm is the focus of this type of sexual act. The wife may or may not feel important to the orgasmic partner.

Masturbating Sex: The addict is fantasizing about either the other person, pornographic movies, books or someone else while having sex with his wife. The primary focus is the person having the orgasm, not his wife. The spouse may feel used, absent or resentful of this sexual encounter.

Violating Sex: This is where the addict demands certain behaviors from their spouse, even though they do not feel comfortable performing them. Although the spouse complies, they hope the addict will stop requesting this particular sexual act. The spouse feels violated as a person and may have anger or resentment toward them for insisting on this particular sexual activity.

Traumatizing Sex: The spouse is forced physically, or with the threat of a weapon or physical pain, to perform a sexual act with the addict. This constitutes rape, and the spouse may feel incredible fear of the perpetrator, as well as feelings of victimization and trauma.

#67
Sexual Systems

As couples evolve together, they create systems for various aspects of their relationship, such as who manages the money, who takes the children to school and who takes out the garbage. Some couples create shared systems or systems may evolve in which one person has total responsibility for one specific area.

It is not uncommon for the addict, who may initiate sex more frequently than their spouse, to end up being totally responsible for the sexual relationship. This leads to discussions, such as "you never initiate sex." The spouse's response to this may be "you never allow me time to." This also leads to the fact that if the addict does all the initiating, they are going to receive 100% of the rejections to be sexual, no matter how little this may actually occur.

Systems, as they evolve with couples, happen slowly and over time. The system around sex is rarely discussed and, hence, usually does not change. Some of the different sex systems that can be created are listed below.

1. Solo System - Only one person initiates having sex, takes all the risk and receives the refusals. This system can lead to only one person's sexual needs being held as important.

2. Scheduled System - The couple decides the frequency of sex they want, whether it is once or several times a week, and a particular partner initiates sex on certain days.

3. Shared System - Both partners are equally responsible for the sexual initiating. The couple decides how to break this up by days, weeks or months.

4. Rotating System - In this system, both partners are responsible to initiate. The couple chooses the frequency of sexual encounters desired in a week or month and then rotates who is responsible to initiate. For example, James and Robin choose to have sex twice a week. They decide to rotate who initiates on a 3-Day schedule. When it is James' turn to initiate, he has three days to manage a convenient time for both of them. When he has initiated, the next day begins Robin's turn to initiate. Neither partner is required to initiate until the last day. Couples like this system, because they feel there is a greater potential to be spontaneous within this system.

In the systems mentioned above, it is not uncommon during the development for one or both partners to be aggressive or passive aggressive in an attempt to resist the change. Some addicts don't like giving up total control of their sex lives, and some wives don't want any sexual responsibility. If this occurs, a system of consequences can be set up for the system you both select. This can be a very sensitive topic. You may need some professional guidance in this area to come to a sexual system agreement and to create consequences or a sense of guidance as you go through this process.

#68
Sexual Assertiveness

Talking to an addict about sexual assertiveness may seem to be an oxymoron. In the addict's addictive lifestyle, they may have been sexually aggressive, passive or manipulative, but rarely assertive.

Being sexually aggressive, demanding or sometimes forceful on your spouse is not healthy and can leave lifelong scars on them. The addict may also avoid their spouse's sexual needs. Depriving your spouse of their sexual needs is also unhealthy. Usually, in this passive system, the spouse has to initiate the sexual encounter. This could also indicate the addict could be an intimacy anorexic as well.

The sexual manipulations of the addict are by far the most prevalent sexual arrangement I see with couples. In this arrangement, hints, winks, massages, touches or a sexual comments are supposed to be interpreted by the spouse as "I would like to have sex with you." Since these hints or comments are not direct, they can be misunderstood, and hence, you may go away mad, because you thought your spouse should be able to read your mind by your manipulations toward wanting to have sex. This system leaves a lot to interpret and can lead to many "you-knew-what-I-meant" arguments about sex.

Sexual <u>assertiveness</u> includes two aspects. The first aspect is asking directly to be sexual with your spouse. The second aspect is having respect for your spouse and realizing that just because you asked for sex doesn't mean you are entitled to what you asked for.

To practice sexual assertiveness, ask your spouse to sit in a chair in front of you, and simply practice several times asking them directly to be sexual. Remember, this is just a practice. Do not actually initiate sex at this time, otherwise, it may feel as if you are being manipulative with them. In this exercise, it is not necessary for your spouse to have any response. After you have asked them several times, switch and allow her to ask you the same question. Remember, this is a practice exercise. Responding in an inappropriate manner may block the progress this exercise can give you. This exercise can be practiced once or twice a day until both of you feel comfortable asking the other to be sexual.

Statements that have worked for other couples are as listed below.

I would like to be sexual with you, would that be convenient for you?
I am feeling sexual and would like to be sexual with you. Can we do this?
Can we be sexual together?
Is being sexual with you an option today or tonight?

Note: Do not practice this exercise in the bedroom or at a time you would normally have sex.

#69
Rejection Desensitization ("Learning to Say No")

Saying "no" to the addict regarding sexual relations can create a big problem for them. This problem has a long history and an explainable origin. In most of the addict's fantasy life and masturbation habits, possibly since early adolescence, they rarely heard the word "no." Every time they wanted to orgasm, they had a willing partner, their fantasy. This distorted reality created a distorted conditioning. In actuality, a healthy spouse may not desire sex every single time they want it. After clocking in hundreds of hours confirming a fantasy with an orgasm, the addict really believes that the fantasy is reality.

This is what causes the addict to blow up, get angry and sometimes find ways to "get even" when their spouse says "no, not tonight." Some addicts go into total rages when rejected sexually. The addict's conditioning is the problem, not their spouse.

When your spouse says "no, not tonight," they are not saying "I hate you." This is the way some addicts interpret what they are saying, and it is not reality. So as an addict, you may need to do some desensitization to realize that your spouse is not rejecting you as a person, but rather they just are not wanting to participate with you sexually at this particular time. They know that there are going to be other times to be sexual together.

The following exercise is a way to help you accept the variety of responses you may receive from your spouse without blowing up after a rejection. It also helps the spouse to practice asking for sexual intimacy, rather than the addict doing 100% of the asking. Do this exercise at a time you would not normally have sex and preferably not in the bedroom. You and your spouse sit face to face, maintaining eye contact. Ask your spouse if you can be sexual with them (see assertiveness exercise). They are to have three responses, which are noted below.

You	Spouse's Response
Would you like to be sexual?	1. Yes, I would like to have sex with you.
Would you like to be sexual?	2. I would like to be sexual at a later time.
Would you like to be sexual?	3. No, I do not want to be sexual at this time.

Practice this several times in one setting, asking a total of nine times. Then switch and have your spouse ask and you give the responses above. This exercise will probably have to be done 10 to 14 times to obtain some level of desensitization.

List below the dates you have practiced this exercise.

_____   _____   _____   _____   _____   _____   _____

_____   _____   _____   _____   _____   _____   _____

#70
Sex Talk

During sexual encounters, it is not uncommon for addicts to disconnect and go into various levels of disassociation. As you recover and desire a healthier, more satisfying sex life, it is important that you nurture and communicate relationally with your spouse during the sexual act. The response I so often receive from addicts is "what do I say while being sexual?" Below is a list of relational statements that may help you through this dilemma.

I love you.

I really have more love for you now than ever.

Thank you for sharing yourself with me.

You're a terrific lover.

I enjoy being with you.

I feel close to you.

I desire you.

I'm glad I'm with you.

I'm proud of you.

I love looking at you.

You are such a comfort to me.

I like growing with you.

I love my life with you.

I thank God you're my wife/husband.

Thank you for loving me.

You are a neat person.

I like you.

I'm glad I married you.

You're beautiful/handsome.

I love your eyes.

#71
Sex: Spirit, Soul And Body

Sex is three dimensional. It is one of the few activities that can touch all three parts of your being, your spirit, soul and body. As an addict, you may have been emotionally and spiritually underdeveloped due to your addiction. Most addicts have only experienced sex in one dimension, which is physically. This may explain the need for more sex almost immediately after having sex. The addict desires three-dimensional sex but is not currently available for this experience.

Most addicts feel they may have perfected the biological aspect of sex. This one-dimensional aspect of sex is what I call "water gun" sex. The development of the other two areas of our being has to occur for us to reach three-dimensional sex. If you are early in your recovery, you may not have any experiential reference point for what I am talking about. After several months into your recovery, you may smile and say, "Oh, that's what he was talking about." After a longer period of sobriety and much hard work in emotional and spiritual development, many addicts will finally have three-dimensional sex.

Tips to working through this three-dimensional sexual process are:

1. Feelings work.
2. Pray alone.
3. Pray with your spouse.
4. Share your feelings with your spouse.
5. Act in a responsible way toward your spouse (do what you say).
6. Practice sexual assertiveness and sex tips in this book.

#72
Sex Tips

During your growing transformation toward relational sex, there are some tips that may help the process get easier. These tips are for you to practice during your sexual encounters to make it more fulfilling for both you and your spouse.

Tip #1: Keep Your Eyes Open - Keeping your eyes open during intercourse makes disconnecting and fantasizing for either spouse more difficult. Disconnecting is the first step to fantasy. Being present emotionally during sex may be uncomfortable at first but will become easier as you both practice.

Tip #2: Keep the Lights On - Having some light on during the sexual encounter is helpful in two ways. First, if it was dark, you couldn't tell, nor would it matter, if your eyes were open since you couldn't see anyway. Secondly, you can keep eye contact with your spouse, which will again keep you from disconnecting and going into fantasy.

Tip #3: Relational Conversation - Having relational conversation (i.e., I love you, you are beautiful) will also keep you focused on the present sexual encounter. Stay away from inappropriate talk; although familiar to many addicts, it may reinforce your addictive, objectifying sex as opposed to reinforcing relational sex with your spouse.

#73
My Sex Plan

In the space below, write out what you believe is your sexual plan. This will help you to be very clear as to what are the current parameters of your sexuality for you and your spouse.

Behaviors my spouse and I agree upon are:

_____   _____

_____   _____

_____   _____

_____   _____

The frequency my spouse and I agree to is: _____

Our agreed upon method of asking for sex is: _____

The responsibility for asking for sex is: _____

Parameters for where we will have sex are:

_____   _____

_____   _____

_____   _____

#74
Professional Counseling

There are several different types of counselors available. Questions to ask a therapist you would consider for counseling are at the end of this exercise. You may want to consider our counseling services mentioned in the back of this book. For those not living within the local area, our services include telephone counseling, telephone groups and 3 and 5 day intensives for addicts, couples and partners.

Along the path of recovery, it may be important or necessary for you to get professional help. This can be a scary reality for you. If the counseling is going to be beneficial for your recovery, it is essential to find someone who is qualified in the area of the addiction you have been struggling with. The stories of what untrained counselors have told people trying to recover from addiction is astounding, regardless if they were psychiatrists, psychologists or master's level counselors.

This is why we have prepared some questions to ask your therapist or doctor before you agree to see them. First, it is important to note that psychiatrists are medical doctors whose primary solution for their client is medicine. Psychologists, social workers and master's level counselors are more counseling oriented in their solutions for their clients. The questions you may want to ask are:

1. How much experience do you have working with _____ addiction?
2. How much of your practice is related to _____ addiction?
3. Do you have specialized training, certification or licensor in _____ addictions?
4. Are you a recovering person who has <u>worked</u> the 12 Steps personally?
5. What books have you read related to _____ addiction?
6. Do you have specific training dealing with sexual abuse issues?

These six questions can be a good start for you to assess the professional you desire to hire to help you recover from your addiction. It is possible, however, in your geographical area to not have a therapist who specializes in addiction.

#75
Read A Book For Partners

If you are an addict, why should you read a book for spouses or family members of addicts? Many addicts are married. During your recovery process, there is a need for change in both spouses within the marital system.

Partners, in general, have little difficulty in buying books on addiction and reading them. In a short period of time, they may know more about your addiction than you. A spouse's book will help you understand the consequences and pain they may be experiencing.

The anger they may have toward you is normal. The grief they go through is normal. The recovery they will go through is a process as well. The more informed you are about their process, the better you will understand that both of you need to recover, so you can both experience a healthy marriage in recovery, as opposed to a marriage in addiction.

You may have to go to a Christian book website or an Amazon type site for specific books related to spouses of your type of addiction.

Date I searched for material for spouses _____

Date I read a book on spouses _____

#76
Step Four

"Made a searching and fearless inventory of ourselves."

Making a personal inventory is helpful in many ways. First, an inventory tells you what has happened and when it happened, both good and harmful. Second, this inventory will give you insight into patterns or cycles of unhealthy behavior. Without this "spreadsheet," you would not be able to see clearly. There are several ways to complete a Fourth Step but all include, in one way or another, writing it down somewhere.

Let's define a few terms first, such as the word "good," which indicates positive things that have happened. "Bad" will mean things you did that you knew were wrong and did them despite this knowledge. A lot of addiction history will fall into this category. "Ugly" will be things that happened to you that you weren't responsible for, such as car accidents, surgeries, parent's divorce, abuse or neglect. With these terms in mind, take a piece of paper, draw your columns and a place for the span of years as seen below, and complete "the rest of the story." Below are some examples.

Years	Good	Bad	Ugly
1-5			
6-10	won spelling bee		placed in foster home
11-15		stole porn	
16-20...			

Behaviors that support a Step Four are as follows.

Behaviors	Yes	No
1. Consistent time spent writing your story	_____	_____
2. Complete honesty on your story	_____	_____
3. Checking in if memories affect sobriety	_____	_____

The day I completed my Fourth Step was _____

"Admitted to God, ourselves, and to another human being the exact nature of our wrongs."

In Step Four, you provided yourself with all the information you need to complete Step Five. Step Four is "your" story. It is a story that has shadows, much like others who are recovering from addiction. This story needs to be admitted to yourself, which usually happens during the writing, reading or sharing of your Fourth Step.

For some, "admitting to God" has been an event all by itself. God already knows, but something can happen when you tell Him where you have been. Some addicts visually put God in an empty chair and read their story to Him. This may be a helpful exercise to do in the process of completing your Fifth Step.

Having "another human being" involved is by far the toughest part. Allowing someone else into your closet of secrets is difficult but entirely necessary for your fullest recovery from addiction. Select a person in the recovery program, a support person of the same sex (not your spouse), a pastor or a therapist to share your story with.

The Fifth Step is a must in your recovery from addiction. While finishing your Fifth Step, you will feel less guilt and shame and begin to experience acceptance, even though you once believed "if someone really knew me, they wouldn't love me." This is not true, and in your Fifth Step, you will get to experience being human, flaws and all.

Behaviors that support a Fifth Step are listed below.

Behaviors	Yes	No
1. A written down Fourth Step	_____	_____
2. A time of reflecting with yourself "admitting to yourself"	_____	_____
3. A time you and God go through "admitting to yourself"	_____	_____
4. Picking someone to share your Fifth Step with	_____	_____
5. Making an appointment to share "your story"	_____	_____
6. Sharing your Story	_____	_____

The day I completed my Fifth Step was _____

#78
Sponsoring Others

Sponsoring, or disciplining others, can be a vital part of your personal recovery from addiction. I cannot tell you how many times God has spoken through me to someone in recovery who needs help. In the Scripture, Jesus stated that in a situation where people are being restored, there He is. I am glad that I have been called to this ministry. Helping another struggling addict will strengthen your faith and remind you of the precious gift you have been given in your recovery.

My experience is that when a Christian gets their addiction into submission, they are truly free and has the ability, by example, to free others. My hope is that as you heal, you will pass the healing along to others.

Growing Up Sexually

You have learned a lot of things growing up in your family. Some of the things you learned are helpful and some are not so helpful. This exercise is going to focus on your family's sexual education. As a child or adolescent, you were taught not only by what your parents said and did but also the attitudes and unwritten rules your parents believed in.

What did you learn about sex from Mom and Dad?

Mom: _____

_____

_____

Dad: _____

_____

_____

From the above information, what beliefs or behaviors have you duplicated in your life? List them below:

_____

_____

_____

What were the long-term results of the sexual beliefs or behaviors that you saw in your parent's life or relationship?

_____

_____

_____

What specific plans can you make so you do not duplicate these same results in your life and relationships?

_____

_____

_____

How to Treat Members of the Opposite Sex

How you treat yourself and others is usually, to some degree, what you have seen or experienced in your family of origin. After forty years, a client recently discovered he created the exact non-intimate relationship his parents had. His personal way of relating had a great deal to do with this.

Patterns of relating to your spouse are taught by your perceptions of your parent's relationship. This can definitely be the case in what you learned about treating your spouse. In the spaces below, write what you learned about treating the opposite sex, both beliefs and behaviors from:

Dad: _____

_____

Mom: _____

_____

From the above lists, are there any beliefs or behaviors you have duplicated in your life? If so, list them below.

_____

_____

What were the long-term results of these beliefs or behaviors about treating others?

_____

_____

What specific plan can you make so you do not duplicate these results in your life and relationships?

_____

_____

Growing Up With Anger

Anger is one thing very few people talk about. As a recovering addict, you will need to discuss and deal with anger from several perspectives. In this section, you will be focusing on what you learned about anger from your parents. In some families, you can only discuss feelings after you get angry. In other words, it is okay to hit or be verbally abusive if you are mad. Many rules about anger are learned in the home, such as don't get mad, ever. Instead, eat or drink alcohol to cope with your anger, run away, withdraw or emotionally punish others with your anger. In the space below, list what you learned about anger regarding beliefs and behaviors from your Mom and Dad.

Mom: _____

_____

Dad: _____

_____

From the above list, are there any beliefs or behaviors you have duplicated in your life? If so, list them.

_____

_____

What were the long-term results of these beliefs or behaviors about anger that you saw in your parent's lifestyle or relationship in the future?

_____

_____

What specific plan can you make not to duplicate these results in your lifestyle and relationship?

_____

_____

#80
My Relationship With Dad

In the space provided, describe your relationship with your Dad as you remember it <u>as a child</u>.

_____

_____

_____

_____

_____

In the space provided, describe your relationship with your Dad as you remember it <u>as a teenager</u>.

_____

_____

_____

_____

_____

In the space provided, describe your relationship with your Dad <u>as an adult</u>.

_____

_____

_____

_____

_____

I feel happy about my relationship with Dad because _____

_____

_____

I feel sad about my relationship with Dad because _____

_____

_____

I feel mad about my relationship with Dad because _____

_____

_____

My hope for my relationship with Dad is _____

_____

_____

_____

In the space below, write a letter to your dad. This letter is for therapeutic purposes only. It is not to be sent to him or seen by him unless you discuss it with your sponsor or therapist. You can express any feelings or situations in your letter, and it may be longer than the space provided.

_____

_____

_____

_____

_____

_____

At different times in your recovery, you will need to confront specific issues. The work you have done in the last few pages may have been difficult and emotional. Your courage to be honest will be a great asset in your recovery.

To confront some of these family of origin issues, it is not necessary that you actually go visit your parents to drag up all the stuff you have been processing and try to dump it on them in a one-time conversation. Dumping on them doesn't have to occur for you to get better or even to confront the past issues. What you are about to do may also be very difficult and emotional. If you feel you may need support by a recovering person or therapist, please do.

Take the "Dear Dad" letter you wrote, and sit in a chair with another chair facing you. When you are ready, read your letter to Dad as if he were right there in the chair across from you. You may or may not experience a wide variety of feelings during this exercise.

This empty chair exercise can further your sense of expression toward your Dad, as well as give you a sense of confronting past feelings or issues. Having these issues addressed can leave you less vulnerable in your addiction recovery.

#81
My Relationship With Mom

In the space provided, describe your relationship with your Mom as you remember it <u>as a child.</u>

_____

_____

_____

In the space below, describe your relationship with your Mom as you remember it <u>as a teenager.</u>

_____

_____

_____

In the space below, describe your relationship with your Mom <u>as an adult.</u>

_____

_____

_____

I feel happy about my relationship with Mom because_____

_____

_____

I feel sad about my relationship with Mom because_____

_____

_____

I feel mad about my relationship with Mom because_____

_____

_____

My hope for my relationship with Mom is_____

_____

_____

#82
My Relationship With God

Now, here is someone you may or may not have met growing up. In your family, your parents may have made God important in a healthy way, a religiously unhealthy way, occasionally important (i.e., holidays and emergencies) or not important at all. No matter what your family did or did not do to introduce you to God, many have their own unique development with God.

In this exercise, you will want to look at what you learned about God from your parents. In the space below, describe what you believe to be your parent's belief and behaviors about God.

Mom's belief and behaviors about God: _____

_____

_____

Dad's belief and behaviors about God: _____

_____

_____

From the above information, are there any beliefs or behaviors that you have duplicated in your life? If so, what are they?

_____

_____

_____

What were the long-term effects of these beliefs or behaviors (good or bad) that you saw in your parent's life or relationship?

_____

_____

_____

What specific plan can you make to avoid these negative results in your life and relationship?

_____

_____

In the space below, describe your relationship with God <u>as a child:</u>

_____

_____

In the space below, describe your relationship with God <u>as a teenager:</u>

_____

_____

_____

In the space below, describe your relationship with God <u>as an adult:</u>

_____

_____

_____

Describe your relationship with God as an adult prior to your recovery from addiction.

_____

_____

_____

In the space provided below, describe your relationship with God as a recovering person.

_____

_____

_____

I'm glad about my relationship with God because: _____

_____

_____

I'm sad about my relationship with God because: _____

_____

_____

I'm mad about my relationship with God because: _____

_____

_____

My wishes about my relationship with God are: _____

_____

_____

_____

In the space below, write a letter to God.

_____

_____

_____

_____

_____

_____

_____

Since we all come from a variety of backgrounds, God may be different for all of us growing up. Most of you will be helped by "a talk with God". In the past pages dealing with family of origin issues, you imagined sitting both Mom and Dad in a chair in front of you and confronted the issues you felt you had with your parents. In this exercise, you can confront specific issues with God. God can be a big relationship in your past, as well as in your recovery. It is very important to be yourself before God in order to move further in your spirituality and relationship with God.

In light of this, take your "Dear God" letter, sit in a chair, and imagine God sitting in the empty chair in front of you. Read your letter to God, and say anything else you feel impressed to say to Him. For some, this exercise may be difficult and may make you feel a wide variety of emotions. If you feel you need the support of a recovering person or a therapist, please do this for your personal well being.

#83
Abuse And Neglects

During your Fourth Step, you made a column titled "ugly." In this section of your Fourth Step, you listed events that happened to you that were not your fault, although they still impacted your life. It is now time to look at these events and begin healing from them as a part of your addiction recovery.

Many addicts have experienced various forms of abuse. Some emotional abuse could consist of being shamed, degraded, humiliated or yelled at regularly. Emotional neglect could involve not being talked to, nurtured, or having someone not care or inquire about how you feel. They may not inquire about your feelings. Physical abuse would include hitting or watching others being hit. Physical neglect would include being improperly clothed or not having adequate food or shelter. Spiritual abuse is sometimes being emotionally or physically abused while your parents justify this by their religious beliefs. Some sexual abuse instances would include exposure to pornography, verbal sexual innuendoes, sexual touches and other behaviors. Sexual neglect is not informing you about your bodily changes and about sex.

In the space provided below, check the areas of abuse and or neglects you feel you have experienced:

Abuses		Neglects	
Emotional	_____	Emotional	_____
Physical	_____	Physical	_____
Spiritual	_____	Spiritual	_____
Sexual	_____	Sexual	_____

#84
My Perpetrators

In the previous exercise, you took a look at the abuses and neglects you may have experienced. In this exercise, you are going to look at the people who were responsible for these abuses and neglects.

I know at this point, you may be going into very painful territory. In fact, so painful that many of these issues may be the very pains you were medicating by acting out in your addiction. It is very important to your healing process that you look at these abuses and neglects you suffered.

In many of the incidences you have experienced, you may have known the perpetrator's name. For some, these events happened in your own home by parents, stepparents, siblings or extended family. In other cases, there may be a casual relationship that preceded the abuse (i.e. a neighbor, schoolteacher or another child at school). For some, the person may be a stranger, and you may not know the perpetrator's name. Maybe it only happened once, and you never saw them again.

Whatever their name or relationship was, these events have been indelibly written into your life. Now, it is time to write down your perpetrator's name (if known), relationship (if any), the type of abuse and an approximate age the abuse/neglect occurred.

Name	Relationship	Abuse/Neglect	Age

#85
What You Did To Me

What you may have experienced from your perpetrator(s) has most likely left you with a lot pain for probably many years. This pain is often free floating inside of you. You may rarely or never talk about what exactly happened, and so, it may remain like an emotional blob of gel that you have not yet crystallized inside.

In your recovery, it will be important to feel this pain, which you have been medicating all these years, and crystallize it as much as possible. It will be very helpful in your recovery to identify what exactly happened and later process your feelings about these events.

In this exercise, you will do exactly that. Crystallize the memory. On the previous page, you wrote down your perpetrators and their general offenses. It is now time to get specific. On a separate piece of paper, list the perpetrator at the top of the page. Write down exactly what your perpetrator did in as much detail as you possibly can.

If you have experienced sexual, physical or other abuses, this will be painful. If you need the support of others, please call to invite others into this healing process with you. If you feel you need professional help at this point, consider a therapist who specializes in this area of recovery.

#86
Ranking My Perpetrator(s)

Ranking your perpetrator(s) may seem like an odd thing to do, after all, any abuse, no matter what kind, should never be experienced by anybody. I know this as well as anyone. As you rank your perpetrator(s), you are not trying to minimize in any way the pain each perpetrator has inflicted on your life.

I compare this exercise process before you to the work of a battle surgeon. Every wound a soldier has is painful, and yet, some wounds will require different levels of procedures, and some wounds may demand more attention than others. We need to outline a plan for surgery, so when you complete your letter and anger work later, your perpetrator(s) will be ranked in order of your perception of who has caused the most damage and pain.

In this exercise, you will need to categorize the perpetrator(s) ranked least abusive and work up to the major traumas, which will require more difficult work from you in the exercises ahead. As you begin working in a ranked order, starting with the least traumatic, you will be stronger, know the process and what to expect a lot better as you move into the higher-ranked, traumatic events.

On the previous page where you listed your perpetrator(s), the abuse/neglect and their age, write next to their name a rank. Start with number one as the least offending and move up to the most severe as the highest ranked abuse.

#87
Letter(s) To My Perpetrator(s)

This exercise takes you a step further into healing from your abuses and/or neglects you may have experienced. Much like what you have already done in creating letters to help you resolve some of the family of origin issues, you now must write a letter to help heal these areas of abuse and neglect.

This letter to each of your perpetrators is for therapeutic purposes only. It is not to be sent to the perpetrator(s). These letters are for your recovery, not theirs. It is important for you to confront the issue, not necessarily the person, especially at this time of recovery. You may have a wide range of feelings as you do this exercise. You may want to solicit the help of a support person and stay in close contact with your group during this time.

In this exercise, imagine having your perpetrator in a room, strapped to a chair. Imagine they couldn't say anything to you, and you could say anything and everything you wanted to them. This letter can be full of hate, anger, disgust and may include other powerful emotions. You can use any language necessary to express yourself. These events should have never happened, so your feelings are totally appropriate.

These letters can be as long as you need in order to fully express yourself. These letters can bring up past feelings and memories. Give yourself permission to feel them, and take as much time as you need. You are worth the time and energy you will need to take on your letters.

Now, write down the name of the perpetrator you ranked "least" on the previous page, and begin to write your letter. After you write your letter, you may want to do an empty chair exercise and read your letter to the perpetrator. If you feel you need a support person present while doing this exercise, please do this for yourself.

If after reading the letter, you feel a sense of resolve, that's great. If you feel there is more work to do, then you may want to consider further assistance from a therapist or support person. There is a specific therapeutic, experiential exercise you can do to relieve trauma issues. This exercise needs to be worked through with a therapist. I have seen many relieved from past physical and sexual trauma issues through this technique offered in our counseling center. Addicts do well to resolve their trauma issues, especially for those where it is the fuel that feeds their addiction.

#88
Step Six

"Were entirely ready to have God remove all these defects of character."

Now that you have written and acknowledged your story to God, yourself and another human being, defects of character may be more obvious to you. In Step Six, you can begin to see some of your limitations or things that are less than positive about yourself. Before you can become "entirely ready," it has been helpful for many addicts to take some reflective time to list their defects of character. Writing down your defects (i.e., impatient, manipulative, selfish) helps you to know what you are preparing to have God remove.

The simplest way to do this is to list in the left-hand column your <u>character defects</u>. Next to the character defect, write the <u>percentage you are willing to have God remove this defect,</u> (i.e., Selfishness, 75%). Review your list regularly until there is a 100% next to each defect. During the start of this list and its completion, you may want to pray over the areas you are less than 100% ready.

Behaviors supporting a Step Six are as follows.

Behaviors	Yes	No
1. A list of "defects of character"	_____	_____
2. A regular review until 100% "entirely ready"	_____	_____
3. Prayer during the process of becoming "entirely ready"	_____	_____
4. Discussions about defects taking longer to be "entirely ready"	_____	_____

Date I became entirely ready to have God remove my defects of character _____

#89
Step Seven

"Humbly asked Him to remove our shortcomings."

You may be very familiar with your shortcomings. Being too familiar with your shortcomings can sometimes make it difficult to get into a humble place and ask God to remove them. In my life, my shortcomings hurt those I loved very much. In looking back, these same shortcomings hurt me too. Shortcomings often need a real miracle to be removed.

I liken this process to that of your child, parent or spouse who might suddenly be diagnosed with a life-threatening disease and all the doctor had to say is "if you pray, now is a good time to do so." Many addicts, regardless of their life history or circumstances, would muster up a "humble-asking" position before God. If someone was watching you, they might call it begging, pleading for God to be merciful "just this once." This is the place to be while completing your Seventh Step.

Asking God to remove your shortcomings is very hard spiritual work. While working on Step Seven, you may want to seriously consider completing just one or two defects a day. More than this may be too draining or may minimize this defect. Some have found it helpful to write down a paragraph or two about how a defect of character has hurt them, as well as others, to assist in humbly asking God to remove them.

Behaviors that support a Step Seven are as follows.

Behaviors	Yes	No
1. List of defects	_____	_____
2. Paragraph of how defects affect you and those that you love.	_____	_____
3. A reflective time	_____	_____
4. A prayer time for each defect	_____	_____

Date I completed praying over each defect _____

#90
The Victims

In any addiction, there are going to be victims. Each addict has led a secret life. In the secret life you lived in, there may be people that you have victimized. You may have victimized sexual partners, your spouse, even your children or other people's children.

These victimizations play a heavy role in guilt and shame. Every day you may live with the faces of innocent people you victimized. In your recovery, there comes a place to deal specifically with the sexual or nonsexual pain you may have caused.

Write down the first names of those you victimized. Place the names and the approximate age you violated them. Keep the work you are doing in a safe place. The courage to face the issues of your sexual inappropriate behavior and victimizations will help you maintain the precious sobriety you have worked so hard for. The past is the past, but you cannot be sober and minimize the pain you may have caused others.

#91
How I Hurt Them

Take the paper you used from the previous exercise, and write down your violation to the victim(s). Take as much time as you need to fully disclose what happened. The violation probably required grooming to get the person to trust you. This grooming is part of the violation. In detail, outline the step-by-step process involved in your victimization. When you get to the actual act of violation, be careful not to write "and then I had sex with them." It may be more appropriate to use anatomical terms.

The truth of what you are going to be writing will be the most rigorously honest and most painful work in the entire process of your recovery. This exercise is essential to help you own and accept these victimizations and may help rid you of any criminal thinking. The victims were in no sense to blame. Deep down you know this, so be as responsible for your behavior as possible. Do this exercise for each victim. If you don't know their name or age, guess their age and give them a name.

#92
Empathy Letter

You have completed some of the hardest work yet, and if you have committed violations against others, you are well aware of the guilt and shame you carry due to this choice of behavior. You need to go one step further in the healing process due to these violations.

Write the victim's name at the top of a piece of paper. After you have done this, begin to write to the victim a letter in regards to how they must have felt spiritually, emotionally, physically and sexually to be victimized by you. Include how the event(s) probably hurt them for a very long time. After completing this part of the letter, you can write anything else you wish to say throughout the remainder of the letter. You can then read it out loud to them by imagining them in an empty chair next to you. You may experience a wide range of emotions at this point. If you feel safer having a support person or a therapist involved in this process, please do so.

When you have finished one of your letters, wait a day or two, and then continue on to the next letter. This process may take a while, don't rush it. You and your recovery are worth every amount of effort you are expending during this phase of your recovery.

#93
Self-Forgiveness

After all the victim empathy letters are completed, there is still more to do. Again, you are to be affirmed for the courage and commitment to your recovery you have mustered up in order to face these very deep and sensitive issues in your life.

During the time of your acting out, and possibly victimizing others, you may have a list of things that you would love to experience forgiveness from. The guilt, shame and fear can be overwhelming when you keep such a list inside of yourself.

Often you are the hardest of all on yourself. You may be limited in your ability to love and accept yourself as an addict. Hopefully, by this time in your recovery, there is a ray of love and hope for yourself.

In this exercise, you have a letter to write also. This time the letter is to you. You are to write a letter of self-forgiveness. You know what you did and what you need to be forgiven for specifically. This process can help you begin a dialog of self-forgiveness for what you have done in your past. Later, this can open the door to truly being free from past pain and guilt.

This letter can be as long as you like. Take your time as you work through this letter. Your recovery is worth it. You can write this letter below on the lines provided or on a separate piece of paper.

_____

_____

_____

_____

_____

_____

_____

_____

#94
But God...

There is one final exercise to complete in order to finish the victimization healing process, and that is your relationship to God. This exercise is similar to the one you just completed. Imagine God in a chair in front of you, and ask God to forgive you of the things you have done. After you have asked for forgiveness from God, imagine switching chairs with Him. You are now to respond as God would. Decide how you want Him to respond to this request of forgiveness you just heard.

After God (that is you) said what He needed to, switch back to the first chair. In this chair, respond to what God said to you.

In the space below, write out God's response and your response back to God.

_____

_____

_____

_____

_____

_____

_____

_____

_____

_____

"Made a list of all persons we have harmed
and became willing to make amends to them all"

Step Eight is yet another one that involves journaling. This step is quite straightforward. List on a piece of paper those you feel you have harmed, especially as it pertains to your addiction.

In the midst of your addiction, you were medicated, unaware of what you were doing and whom you were hurting. Now in your recovery, you are sober enough to know your acting-out behaviors have a price to pay. If you need help with this list, consult your Fourth Step. Most people on your "bad" list column will qualify for this list in Step Eight.

After you make your list, put a percentage next to it representing how currently ready you are to make an amend to this person, (i.e. Joe, 75%). Review your list regularly until all people on your list have 100% next to them. This exercise may take prayer and reflection until all people have a 100% next to their name. Step Eight is just to move us to be "willing".

Behaviors that support Step Eight are as follows.

Behaviors	Yes	No
1. A list of persons harmed	_____	_____
2. Percentages that increase	_____	_____
3. Prayer and reflection	_____	_____
4. Discussion with support people over difficult issues	_____	_____

Date I completed Step Eight _____

#96

Step Nine

"Made direct amends to such people wherever possible, except when to do so would injure them or others."

This step does take into consideration those to whom your direct amends "may" injure. This part of the step is not a loophole so that you don't have to make an amend. If you feel you have such a situation, talk with two people who have completed Step Eight and/or a therapist. If they agree with you, then this is probably a legitimate situation not to make an amend.

The rest of this step is quite simple to do. With the list you have from Step Nine, write next to each name the most direct approach to do your amend, whether face to face, by phone call or letter (i.e., Joe, person several states away - phone call). The issue of contacting past sexual partners should be discussed with your sponsor or a therapist before contacting them.

When your list of people and contact methods are complete, you are ready to start. Writing down the date you completed your amend is helpful to keep you motivated to finish the entire list. A complete entry might look like this.

Joe: Father-in-Law   Face to face method   Date completed: 01-12-00

Behaviors that support a Step Nine are as follows.

Behaviors	Yes	No
1. List of people	_____	_____
2. Method of contact list	_____	_____
3. Discussion with sponsor or therapist about those you have questions about contacting	_____	_____
4. Regular progress	_____	_____
5. A completed list	_____	_____

Date I completed Step Nine _____

Part 3

Maintaining Recovery Techniques

#97
Step Ten

"Continued to take personal inventory and when we were wrong, promptly admit it."

Continuing to do anything means you have already started doing something. Congratulations! You are entering what some call the "maintenance" part of the Twelve Step process. Step Ten does not allow you to have secrets in your closet, especially now that you put all your time and energy into cleaning it out.

Keeping a healthy recovery is a discipline. In this step, journaling a daily personal inventory is your tool to make sure you are "staying clean" with yourself and others. In this step, you will reflect daily with yourself and ask the following: "Is there anything I did today that I know wasn't honest or right?" If so, make an amend to this person.

Those who are married or have children will find a lot of opportunities to practice your recovery and stay humble. When this process is integrated, it can provide a lifestyle of honesty for your own well being and integrity with others.

Behaviors that support a Step Ten are as follows.

Behaviors	Yes	No
1. Daily reflection	_____	_____
2. Check off your findings for the day	_____	_____
3. Check off daily any offenses made (remember, "promptly")	_____	_____
4. Ongoing discussions about steps with sponsor or therapist	_____	_____

Date I completed Step Ten _____

#98
Develop New Interests

Exercise

In recovery, the tool of "physical exercise" can help in several ways. Exercise releases natural opiates to the brain. This gives your brain an alternative way (other than acting out) to receive its "brain cookies." Regular exercise can reactivate a neurological pathway you had as a teenager. It can help shift the brain's dependency of acting out as its primary "brain cookie," and rely more on exercise.

Secondly, exercise can help you release stress. This release may help you stay more focused in your recovery. Exercise can help you maintain a more positive outlook and have increased energy to work on recovery issues, such as relating to others.

Thirdly, consistent exercise can give you a sense of accomplishment. This can help your self-esteem. The more you like yourself, the less likely you are to want to hurt yourself, including acting out in your addiction.

Exercise is an essential part of recovery. In treatment centers for addiction, trained professionals encourage clients to exercise regularly while in treatment. As in all exercise, it starts off slow. Get your doctor's approval, and above all, make it fun. I personally find 20 to 30 minutes of aerobic activity makes a significant difference.

Make a list of your exercise activities for the next 90 days, including the days of the week and the times you will exercise. If you need someone for accountability, write down that person's name.

Note: Exercise can be combined with re-socializing yourself also. There are clubs for running, biking, volleyball and softball leagues, etc. Check your yellow pages and call or visit your local YMCA. Also, be aware of your boundaries as you venture into public places.

Developing New Interests

As an addict, you may have slowly drifted into a small, isolated world. In this isolated world, your primary fix was your spouse, children, work acquaintances and your addiction, rarely in that order. I can't tell you how many addicts have told me their thoughts and behaviors are primarily motivated by their addiction. This does not leave much time and money for the pursuit of things you used to do. As your addiction takes over your life, usually hobbies and relationships go to the side, unless they were a cover up for your addiction or a way to obtain access to your victims.

In recovery, as you move past the survival stage, you will need to have a balance of social and personal activities. There is no magical way to make this happen. First, make a list of activities you used to enjoy and a list of things you think you might enjoy. Secondly, find out where you have to go to do these activities. Thirdly, go a few times, and if you like it, add this activity as part of your life recovery plan. Again, be aware of your boundaries, and discuss this with an accountability person or a therapist.

#99
Step Eleven

"Sought through prayer and meditation to improve our conscious contact with God as we understood Him, praying only for the knowledge of His will for us and the power to carry that out."

Prayer has been said to be "talking to God," whether it be requests, petitions, complaints, feelings and whatever other thoughts you might want to share in your personal relationship with God. Meditation is the point after you have quieted down and actually listen to hear what is on His mind. Both prayer and meditation are important. You have already established some type of relationship with God. This is a time to strengthen or improve that relationship.

Asking God for His will may be unfamiliar at first, but as you do it, you will realize His will always has your best interest at heart. He is a Father who loves you dearly. Since He takes the time and energy to communicate His will for you, it is my experience that He will give you the power to carry it out. This may be unfamiliar at first, but this step allows you to practice hearing and following through with God. This can open up a whole new aspect to your spiritual life, which will enhance your recovery from addiction.

Behaviors that support a Step Eleven are as follows.

Behaviors	Yes	No
1. A regular time with God	_____	_____
2. Journal what God is saying	_____	_____
3. Keeping track of following God's will and the results	_____	_____
4. Increased reading and discussing spiritual matters	_____	_____

Date I completed Step Eleven _____

#100
Step Twelve

"Having had a spiritual awakening as a result of these steps, we tried to carry this message to others and to practice these principles in all our affairs."

I enjoy receiving results, no matter what the activity or area of my life I am working on, especially when the results are obvious. Your recovery has included a lot of hard emotional work and self-discovery. It is through these steps that you had a "spiritual awakening."

You now have something to share. I was an addict, damaging myself and others. Now, through this process, I am not acting out, and for the first time, I am able to look at others and myself. There are people throughout your life who will need this message of hope. When these people come across your path, through whatever circumstances, share your strength, hope and experience with them.

To be able to practice honesty, integrity and spirituality is a gift, which your recovery from addiction has given to you. To keep sobriety is to keep practicing what you learned in your steps, which have given you abstinence from your behavior.

Behaviors that support Step Twelve are as follows.

Behaviors	Yes	No
1. Continued abstinence from acting out	_____	_____
2. Continued honesty and integrity	_____	_____
3. Continued amends when they are due	_____	_____
4. A lifestyle of healthy relationships	_____	_____

Date I completed Step Twelve _____

#101
Giving It Away

In a study of alcoholics who were followed for ten years by a researcher, he found there were only two variables, which set apart the recovering alcoholic still sober for ten years and the alcoholics who went back to drinking. One of the two variables, which separated the successful recovering alcoholic from the unsuccessful, was the successful recovering alcoholic regularly attended their 12-Step Support Group, Alcoholics Anonymous. The second variable was the fact that these successful recovering alcoholics sponsored people in AA. In a sense, they were "giving it away." You will hear in support groups time and time again "to keep it, you have to give it away." This is now a scientific fact.

As you recover from addiction, you will find great changes occurring in your life. Your return to sanity will probably affect all areas of your life spiritually, socially and sexually.

If you would like to start a Recovery Group in your church, you can "give it away" to other members (addicts are in every church, guaranteed) and to those in your community. Many need recovery so badly they will even go to a church group if it would help! You will see the Lord naturally send people to you who need your help. When their lives become as changed as yours, you will experience the same joy I see daily in my life. May God bless your journey toward recovery.

Dr. Doug

Appendix

Feelings Exercise

1. I feel (put feeling word here) when (put a present situation when you feel this).
2. I first remember feeling put the same feeling word here when earliest occurrence of this feeling.

Abandoned	Attractive	Childlike	Demoralized	Exhilarated	Hollow
Abused	Aware	Choked-up	Dependent	Exposed	Honest
Aching	Awestruck	Close	Depressed	Fake	Hopeful
Accepted	Badgered	Cold	Deprived	Fascinated	Hopeless
Accused	Baited	Comfortable	Deserted	Feisty	Horrified
Accepting	Bashful	Comforted	Desirable	Ferocious	Hostile
Admired	Battered	Competent	Desired	Foolish	Humiliated
Adored	Beaten	Competitive	Despair	Forced	Hurried
Adventurous	Beautiful	Complacent	Despondent	Forceful	Hurt
Affectionate	Belligerent	Complete	Destroyed	Forgiven	Hyper
Agony	Belittled	Confident	Different	Forgotten	Ignorant
Alienated	Bereaved	Confused	Dirty	Free	Ignored
Aloof	Betrayed	Considerate	Disenchanted	Friendly	Immature
Aggravated	Bewildered	Consumed	Disgusted	Frightened	Impatient
Agreeable	Blamed	Content	Disinterested	Frustrated	Important
Aggressive	Blaming	Cool	Dispirited	Full	Impotent
Alive	Bonded	Courageous	Distressed	Funny	Impressed
Alone	Bored	Courteous	Distrustful	Furious	Incompetent
Alluring	Bothered	Coy	Distrusted	Gay	Incomplete
Amazed	Brave	Crabby	Disturbed	Generous	Independent
Amused	Breathless	Cranky	Dominated	Gentle	Insecure
Angry	Bristling	Crazy	Domineering	Genuine	Innocent
Anguished	Broken-up	Creative	Doomed	Giddy	Insignificant
Annoyed	Bruised	Critical	Doubtful	Giving	Insincere
Anxious	Bubbly	Criticized	Dreadful	Goofy	Isolated
Apart	Burdened	Cross	Eager	Grateful	Inspired
Apathetic	Burned	Crushed	Ecstatic	Greedy	Insulted
Apologetic	Callous	Cuddly	Edgy	Grief	Interested
Appreciated	Calm	Curious	Edified	Grim	Intimate
Appreciative	Capable	Cut	Elated	Grimy	Intolerant
Apprehensive	Captivated	Damned	Embarrassed	Grouchy	Involved
Appropriate	Carefree	Dangerous	Empowered	Grumpy	Irate
Approved	Careful	Daring	Empty	Hard	Irrational
Argumentative	Careless	Dead	Enraged	Harried	Irked
Aroused	Caring	Deceived	Enraptured	Hassled	Irresponsible
Astonished	Cautious	Deceptive	Enthusiastic	Healthy	Irritable
Assertive	Certain	Defensive	Enticed	Helpful	Irritated
Attached	Chased	Delicate	Esteemed	Helpless	Isolated
Attacked	Cheated	Delighted	Exasperated	Hesitant	Jealous
Attentive	Cheerful	Demeaned	Excited	High	Jittery

Joyous	Positive	Scorned	Suffocated	Used
Lively	Powerless	Scrutinized	Sure	Useful
Lonely	Present	Secure	Sweet	Useless
Loose	Precious	Seduced	Sympathy	Unworthy
Lost	Pressured	Seductive	Tainted	Validated
Loving	Pretty	Self-centered	Tearful	Valuable
Low	Proud	Self-conscious	Tender	Valued
Lucky	Pulled apart	Selfish	Tense	Victorious
Lustful	Put down	Separated	Terrific	Violated
Mad	Puzzled	Sensuous	Terrified	Violent
Maudlin	Quarrelsome	Sexy	Thrilled	Voluptuous
Malicious	Queer	Shattered	Ticked	Vulnerable
Mean	Quiet	Shocked	Tickled	Warm
Miserable	Raped	Shot down	Tight	Wary
Misunderstood	Ravished	Shy	Timid	Weak
Moody	Ravishing	Sickened	Tired	Whipped
Morose	Real	Silly	Tolerant	Whole
Mournful	Refreshed	Sincere	Tormented	Wicked
Mystified	Regretful	Sinking	Torn	Wild
Nasty	Rejected	Smart	Tortured	Willing
Nervous	Rejuvenated	Smothered	Touched	Wiped out
Nice	Rejecting	Smug	Trapped	Wishful
Numb	Relaxed	Sneaky	Tremendous	Withdrawn
Nurtured	Relieved	Snowed	Tricked	Wonderful
Nuts	Remarkable	Soft	Trusted	Worried
Obsessed	Remembered	Solid	Trustful	Worthy
Offended	Removed	Solitary	Trusting	
Open	Repulsed	Sorry	Ugly	
Ornery	Repulsive	Spacey	Unacceptable	
Out of control	Resentful	Special	Unapproachable	
Overcome	Resistant	Spiteful	Unaware	
Overjoyed	Responsible	Spontaneous	Uncertain	
Overpowered	Responsive	Squelched	Uncomfortable	
Overwhelmed	Repressed	Starved	Under control	
Pampered	Respected	Stiff	Understanding	
Panicked	Restless	Stimulated	Understood	
Paralyzed	Revolved	Stifled	Undesirable	
Paranoid	Riled	Strangled	Unfriendly	
Patient	Rotten	Strong	Ungrateful	
Peaceful	Ruined	Stubborn	Unified	
Pensive	Sad	Stuck	Unhappy	
Perceptive	Safe	Stunned	Unimpressed	
Perturbed	Satiated	Stupid	Unsafe	
Phony	Satisfied	Subdued	Unstable	
Pleasant	Scared	Submissive	Upset	
Pleased	Scolded	Successful	Uptight	

Time/Cost Card

Age	Hours in Addiction (Weekly)	Multiply by 260 (52wks x 5 yrs)	Hourly Rate at the Time	Total Dollar Amount
15-20				
20-25				
25-30				
30-35				
35-40				
40-45				
45-50				
50-55				
55-60				
60+				

Total time in monetary value_____

Other Costs

Drug of Choice   _____
Therapy   _____
Guilt Offerings   _____
Legal Fees   _____
Divorce/Child Support   _____
Lost Business/Ed.Opportunity   _____
Other   _____

Subtotal_____   Overall Total Cost _____

The Twelve-Steps of Alcoholics Anonymous

1. We admitted we were powerless over alcohol–that our lives had become unmanageable.

2. Came to believe that a Power greater than ourselves could restore us to sanity.

3. Made a decision to turn our will and our lives over to the care of God as we understood Him.

4. Made a searching and fearless moral inventory of ourselves.

5. Admitted to God, to ourselves, and to another human being the exact nature of our wrongs.

6. Were entirely ready to have God remove all these defects of character.

7. Humbly asked Him to remove our shortcomings.

8. Made a list of all people we had harmed, and became willing to make amends to them all.

9. Made direct amends to such people where ever possible, except when to do so would injure them or others.

10. Continued to take personal inventory, and when we were wrong, promptly admitted it.

11. Sought though prayer and meditation to improve our conscious contact with God as we understood Him, praying only for knowledge of His will for us and the power to carry that out.

12. Having had a spiritual awakening as the result of these steps, we tried to carry this message to others and to practice these principles in all our affairs.

The Twelve-Steps reprinted for adaptation by permission of AA World Services, Inc. Copyright 1939.

The Twelve-Steps of Alcoholics Anonymous
Adapted for Addicts

1. We admitted we were powerless over our addiction—that our lives had become unmanageable.

2. Came to believe that a Power greater than ourselves could restore us to sanity.

3. Made a decision to turn our will and our lives over to the care of God as we understood Him.

4. Made a searching and fearless moral inventory of ourselves.

5. Admitted to God, to ourselves, and to another human being the exact nature of our wrongs.

6. Were entirely ready to have God remove all these defects of character.

7. Humbly asked God to remove our shortcomings.

8. Made a list of all people we had harmed, and became willing to make amends to them all.

9. Made direct amends to such people wherever possible, except when to do so would injure them or others.

10. Continued to take personal inventory, and when we were wrong, promptly admitted it.

11. Sought through prayer and meditation to improve our conscious contact with God as we understood Him, praying only for knowledge of His will for us and the power to carry that out.

12. Having had a spiritual awakening as the result of these steps, we tried to carry this message to others and to practice these principles in all our day to day living.

COUNSELING

*"Without the intensive, my marriage would have ended and I would not have known why.
Now I am happier than ever and my marriage is bonded permanently."*

Counseling Sessions

Couples are helped through critical phases of disclosure moving into the process of recovery, and rebuilding trust in relationships. We have helped many couples rebuild their relationship and grasp and implement the necessary skills for an intimate relationship.

Individual counseling offers a personal treatment plan for successful healing in your life. In just one session a counselor can help you understand how you became stuck and how to move toward freedom.

Partners of sex addicts need an advocate. Feelings of fear, hurt, anger, betrayal, and grief require a compassionate, effective response. We provide that expert guidance and direction. We have helped many partners heal through sessions that get them answers to their many questions including: "How can I trust him again?"

A counseling session today can begin your personal journey toward healing.

3 and 5 Day Intensives

in Colorado Springs, Colorado
are available for the following issues:

- Sexual Addiction
- Marriage
- Pastors
- Partners of Sexual Addicts
- Intimacy Anorexia
- Victims of Sexual Abuse
- Adult Children of Sex Addicts
- Teenage Children of Sex Addicts
- Teens

Attendees of Intensives will receive:

- Personal attention from counselors who specialize in your area of need

- An understanding of how the addiction /anorexia and its consequences came into being

- Three counseling sessions daily

- Daily assignments to increase the productiveness of these daily sessions

- Individuals get effective counseling to recover from the effects of sexual addiction, abuse and intimacy anorexia.

- Addiction, abuse, anorexia issues are thoroughly addressed for couples and individuals. This includes the effects on the partner or family members of the addict, and how to rebuild intimacy toward a stronger relationship.

NEW RELEASES

Five Sex Languages

Is unique, not only to increase sexual pleasure but to increase understanding your partner sexually. Once you learn your spouse's sex language, giving them pleasurable sex for a lifetime will be easier than ever. $16.95

Worthy

This Series is designed for anyone who has struggled with doubting their amazing worth. This insightful and pragmatic journey to worthy is one every believer should experience. You are worth this journey to see what others see - your worth! $29.95

MEN'S RECOVERY

THE FINAL FREEDOM

DOUGLAS WEISS, PH.D.

This book gives more current information than many professional counselors have today on sexual addiction. $22.95

101 FREEDOM EXERCISES

DOUGLAS WEISS, PH.D.

This workbook will outline the best techniques to help obtain freedom from sexual addiction. $39.95

STEPS TO FREEDOM

DOUGLAS WEISS, PH.D.

This step book is specifically written for the person desiring recovery from sexual addiction. $14.95

Helping Her Heal

Douglas Weiss, Ph.D.

Offers practical tools for hearing her pain, navigating her grief and losses, discovering her expectations of you and the boundaries she may need to heal. $69.95

6 TYPES OF SEX ADDICTS

DOUGLAS WEISS, PH.D.

This CD will give you more information than most therapists have on sexual addiction. You will be able to finally know how you became a sexual addict and identify why you might still be relapsing. $29.95

TREATMENTS FOR THE

6 TYPES OF SEX ADDICTS

DOUGLAS WEISS, PH.D.

Once you know the type of sex addict you are, Dr. Doug outlines the same treatment plan you would receive in an individual session. $29.95

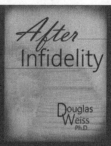

After Infidelity

Douglas Weiss Ph.D.

Helps identify key points about the whys of infidelity, the types of cheaters, and how to start walking toward a healthy marriage. $49.95

Addict to Addict
Douglas Weiss, Ph.D.

This amazing DVD has 8 addicts telling their stories through directed questions. These individuals address key issues along with their journey through recovery. $19.95

making amends
Doing it well the first time

Lori Dravecky

Making Amends was created for men who are working through their sexual addiction recovery and have reached Step 9 where they make amends to their wife. $19.95

www.drdougweiss.com   719.278.3708

WOMEN'S RECOVERY

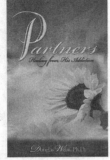

This book offers the readers hope, along with a plan for recovery. Any woman who is a partner of a sex addict will find this book a necessity for her journey toward healing. $14.95

This is like therapy in a box for women who want to walk through the residual effects of being in a relationship with a sex addict. $39.95

This is an interactive workbook that allows the partners of sex addicts to gain insight and strength through working the Twelve Steps. $14.95

This DVD set is for any woman who is currently or was in a relationship with a sexual addict. If anger is still an issue, this material can help with her healing. $29.95

In this DVD set Dr. Weiss will expose the viewer to specific reasons as to why men lie and helpful strategies to end the lying. $44.95

Your pain and betrayal are real and are addressed in this DVD series. You deserve the best answer to your questions and in just under 2 hours you can have them answered for you. $69.95

This CD series addresses all three aspects of a couple recovering from the impacts of sexual addiction. $19.95

This amazing DVD has 8 partners of sex addicts telling their stories through directed questions. A must DVD for every spouse of a sex addict. $19.95

This 2 hour DVD set was produced for divorced women who desire to date again. $29.95

www.drdougweiss.com 719.278.3708

INTIMACY ANOREXIA

This hidden addiction is destroying so many marriages today. In your hands is the first antidote for a person or spouse with anorexia to turn the pages on this addiction process. $22.95

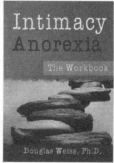

This is like therapy in a box. Inside is 100 exercises that have already been proven helpful in treating intimacy anorexia. $39.95

This is the only twelve step workbook just for intimacy anorexia. Each step gives you progress in your healing from intimacy anorexia. $14.95

This book will not only unlock the understanding of intimacy anorexia but you will also hear experiences of spouses who have found themselves married and alone. $14.95

This is the first workbook to offer practical suggestions and techniques to better navigate through recovery from your spouse's Intimacy Anorexia. $39.95

These Steps can further your healing and recovery from your spouse's Intimacy Anorexia. $14.95

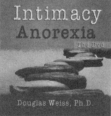

This DVD will give you the characteristics, causes and strategies of intimacy anorexia. This DVD also provides solutions for the intimacy anorexic to start their road to recovery. $69.95

This DVD is for the spouse of an intimacy/sexual anorexic. Dr. Weiss will help you to start a journey of recovery from living with a spouse with intimacy anorexia. $49.95

Everyone has an unlimited number of emotions, but few have been trained to identify, choose, communicate, and master them. $16.95

www.drdougweiss.com 719.278.3708

MARRIAGE

In these pages you will walk with God as He creates the man, the woman and his masterpiece called marriage. $16.95

This is an eight week marriage training that actually gives you the skills to have a healthy more vibrant marriage. $59.95

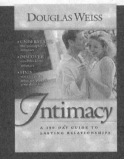

This 100 Day guide can transform couples from any level of intimacy to a lifestyle of satiation with their spouse. $11.99

Dr. Weiss walks you through the creation and maintenance of your marriage. $12.95

This book helps develop faithfulness, patience, forgiveness, service, respect, kindness, and celebration, all of which contribute to an exciting, loving and wonderful relationship. $13.99

By taking ten minutes a day to focus on each other, you can enhance your marriage in ways you'll appreciate for a lifetime. $14.99

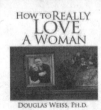

In this 12 part DVD series, you will be exposed to tried and true principles to help you learn how to really love a woman. $69.00

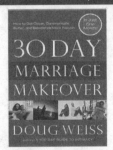

30-Day Marriage Makeover shows you how to energize your relationship and create the intimacy that you long for. $16.99

These DVD are a must for every Christian men and woman. You are practically and passionately walked through Christian sexuality that really works. $29.95(each)

OTHER RESOURCES

"Born for War" teaches practical tools to defeat these sexual landmines and offers scriptural truths that empower young men to desire successfulness in the war thrust upon them. $29.95

This 2 hour DVD helps single women ages 15-30, to successfully navigate through the season of dating. $29.95

This 2 Disc DVD Series is definitely nothing you have heard before. Dr. Weiss charts new territory as to the why for sexual purity. $29.95

A gift for your daugher as she enters college. Letters to my Daughter includes my daily letters to my daughter during her first year of college. $14.95

Erin discovers she comes from a long line of dragons, dragons who have effectively maintained Earth's balance since the planet's beginning. Will she accept her fate and responsibility? $14.95

Within these pages of this book you will find a tried and true path for recovery from any addiction. Here you will get a biblical understanding to break the strongholds in your life forever. $22.95

This workbook provides tips, biblical principles, techniques, and assignments that Dr. Weiss has given his addicted clients with any addiction for over twenty-five years. $39.95

These steps were derived from a Christian perspective and offer much needed insight and practical wisdom to help you get free and stay free from any addiction. $14.95

This Dvd series includes leadership training and fifty segments that are about 10 minutes in length. Churches of any size can begin a Recovery for Everyone group in their local church. $99.00

www.drdougweiss.com 719.278.3708

CLEAN RESOURCES

Every Christian man is born into a sexual war. The enemy attacks the young, hoping to scar them permanently and leave them ruined. But your past is not enough to keep you from the enduringly clean life you want and deserve. $16.99

This journal is designed to be used in conjunction with the Clean book and the Clean DVD set. This set can be used individually or in a church small group or accountability group. $14.99

This DVD set exposes you to many tried and true spiritual truths with very practical applications. You and your church are about to take an amazing journey towards God's insights for your freedom. $29.99

LUST FREE RESOURCES

Every man can fight for and obtain a lust free lifestyle. Once you know how to stop lust, you will realize how weak lust really can be. God gave you the power to protect those you love from the ravages of lust for the rest of your life! It's time to take it back! $13.95

This DVD series walks you through how every man can fight for and obtain a lust free lifestyle. Once you know how to stop lust, you will realize how weak lust really can be. God gave you the power to protect those you love from the ravages of lust for the rest of your life! It's time to take it back! $23.95

FREE APP!
Download Now!

Get it on Google play

Available on the App Store

CONFERENCES

What an incredible way to deliver such a sensitive, "hush hush" topic!! Thank you from the bottom of my heart. I really enjoyed tonight's conference. Today will count as the first day of my sexual sobriety.

CLEAN is a powerful men's conference equipping men to join the battle to maintain sexual purity. In this conference, men will be given tools and biblical principles so they can get started immediately.

PURITY Mixed audiences can be impacted by Successfully Single, as well as Born for War for Male Teens and Princes take Longer than Frogs for Female Teens to help motivate them to fight for their sexual purity.

MEN The Sex, Men & God conferences is where men experience great personal growth and understanding into their sexuality...where other speakers rarely go. How to Really Love a Woman is really practical training for the men in your church.

COUPLES attending the Intimacy, 10 Minute Marriage or The 7 Love Agreements Conference discover how to discuss their desires, learn the importance of marital dating, how to connect emotionally, how to let go of your past and much more.

WOMEN How to Really Love a Man and Best Sex for Women are great inspiring and practical teachings for the women in your church.

For additional conference information, including available dates, please call our office at 719-278-3708, visit our website at www.drdougweiss.org or you may also email us at conferences@drdougweiss.org

A A S A T™

American Association for Sex Addiction Therapy

Sexual Recovery Coach (SRC)™

Become a certified SRC (Sexual Recovery Coach) by successfully completing all 45 hours of the AASAT Sex Addiction Training Program and a qualifying Life Coaching education. AASAT has created a 45-hour program to train life coaches how to work with sexual addicts and partners of sexual addicts. Being a sexual addiction coach is a two step process. This includes completing the AASAT training (45 hours of DVD'S, worksheets and 6 months of telephone supervision with Dr. Doug or other trained supervisors) and an approved life coach training which can take about 6 to 8 months, AASAT includes training to coach partners as well as addicts. Both need to be fully completed to become a certified SRC (Sexual Recovery Coach).

* Life coaching is not counseling. Therapists diagnose and treat a problem. Life coaching is a positive process to help one's goal in recovery.

Sexual Recovery Therapist (SRT)™

AASAT has designed a training program with you in mind! Become an SRT (Sex Recovery Therapist) in the privacy of your own home or office. The days of traveling for conferences, supervision and continuing education hours are over! You're in control of when and how long you take to complete your training. Watch and review your training DVD's as often as needed to gain valuable information and skills in one of the fastest growing clinical issues of our day, sexual addiction. This program is designed with the therapist in mind, who is working in an outpatient setting and needing practical information on treating sexually addicted clients, their partners and family members. Each participant will receive a certification of completion suitable for framing.

With this AASAT training, you will gain proven clinical insight into treating addictive behaviors involving pornography, prostitutes, multiple affairs, plus training on counseling their partners and adult children. Both men and women are seeking counseling more than ever for sexually addictive behaviors.

Sexual Recovery Pastoral Counselor

This program is designed with the pastoral counselor in mind, who is working in a church/clinical setting and needing practical information on treating sexually addicted clients, their partners and family members. Becoming an SRPC distinguishes you as a pastoral counselor who can more completely treat sexual addiction in your church and community. This certification requires: Masters degree or 5 years Ordained Pastoral Experience

Get Certified:

Now you can become an SRT™ (Sex Recovery Therapist). There's a great need in every community for a therapist who specializes in sexual addiction recovery. Becoming an SRT™ distinguishes you as a therapist who can more completely treat sexual addiction in your community.

Get Certificate of Completion:

Anyone can learn more about sexual addiction and its impact. Recovering people, clergy and others have benefited tremendously by taking this course. Upon completion you receive a certificate demonstrating completion of this course and a commitment to help those in recovery.

The Sex Addiction Training course includes 45 DVD's and a workbook including bibliography.

For Just: $795

(that's less than $18.00 per hour!)
Payment options available!

Call 719.330.2425
or visit www.aasat org

Partner's Recovery Training

Become a PRT® (Partner's Recovery Therapist) in the privacy of your own home or office. The days of traveling for conferences, supervision, and continuing education hours are over! You are in control of when and how long you take to complete your training. Watch and review your training DVDs as often as needed to gain valuable information and skills in treating partners of sexual addicts. This program is designed with the therapist in mind who works in an outpatient setting and needs practical information on treating partners of sexual addicts. Each participant will receive certification of completion suitable for framing after completing the training. This can be a great way to earn continuing education hours as well.

If you are currently certified by another organization to treat sexual addiction, this training will complement that training. Dr. Weiss developed this program utilizing his own proven methodology and modality, as well as his clinical application for treating partners of sexual addicts for over 25 years. With this AASAT training, you will gain proven clinical insight into treating the issues facing partners. You can be prepared! Over thirty hours of topics related to partners treatment are covered in this training, including:

- Partner Model
- Partner Grief
- Anger
- Boundaries
- Partners as Intimacy Anorexics

- Reactive Intimacy Anorexia
- Partner Worthlessness
- Polygraph Questions
- Separation
- Sex in Recovery

The Partner's Recovery Training course includes 31 DVDs and a workbook including bibliography.

For Just: $595.00

(that's less than $19.00 per hour!)

COMING SOON!!!
INTIMACY ANOREXIA TRAINING

Become a IAT®(Intimacy Anorexia Therapist) in the privacy of your own home or office. The days of traveling for conferences, supervision and continuing education hours are over! You are in control of when and how long you take to complete your training. Watch and review your training DVDs as often as needed to gain valuable information and skills in one of the fastest growing clinical issues of our day, intimacy anorexia. This program is designed with the therapist in mind who works in an outpatient setting and needs practical information on treating intimacy anorexic clients and their partners. Each participant will receive certification of completion suitable for framing for completing the training. This can be a great way to earn continuing education hours as well.

Dr. Weiss developed this program utilizing his own proven methodology and modality, as well as his clinical application for treating intimacy anorexia. With this AASAT training, you will gain proven clinical insight into treating intimacy anorexia behaviors, plus training on counseling their partners. Both men and women are seeking counseling more than ever for intimacy anorexia behaviors. You can be prepared! Thirty hours of topics related to intimacy anorexia treatment are covered in this training including:

- Defining Intimacy Anorexia
- Charateristics of Intimacy Anorexia
- Friends of Intimacy Anorexia
- Sex and Recovery
- Partners Issues

- Behavioral Treatment
- Assessment Tools
- Comorbidity Issues
- Treatment Strategies
- Intimacy Anorexia Grief and Anger

PRE ORDER: The Intimacy Anorexia Training course includes over 30 DVD's and a workbook including bibliography.

For Just: $695

Recovery Meetings

1. Any new members are introduced by the point person and are asked to verbalize the Recovery Covenant to the group in the first person. (For example, I covenant to...)

2. Introductions - Beginning with the chairperson of the meeting, introductions are done as follows: The chairperson introduces themselves, shares their feelings, their boundaries and length of time free from those behaviors.

Example:
"My name is John. I feel frustrated and alone. My boundaries to stay free are no pornography, bookstores, and no sex outside of marriage. I worked on Exercises Nos. 5-7 in my Freedom for Everyone workbook and made four pages of progress on my Steps to Recovery workbook since our last meeting. I have been free for 3 weeks."

3. The *chairperson* chooses a topic related to staying free from being driven by addiction that the group discusses. Each member can share without feedback from the group, unless feedback is specifically asked for by the sharing member.

4. Honest Time - Group members break off into groups of two to three members and discuss thoughts, behaviors, struggles and successes since the last meeting (James 5:16).

5. Closing Prayer - Group members come back together to repeat the Lord's Prayer.

Recovery Group Materials

1. *Freedom For Everyone*
2. *Freedom For Everyone: Workbook*
3. *Freedom for Everyone: Steps*

Freedom Group Topics for Discussion

Triggers	Honesty	God's Grace
Fear	Hope	Exercise
Bottom Lines	Relapse	Intimacy
Control	H.A.L.T.	Steps 1-12
Boundaries	Prayer	Maximized Thinking
Recovery Rituals	Feelings	Anger
Dangerous Dabbling	Fun	Father Issues
Sexual Abuse	Grooming Victims	Objectifying
Accountability	Discipline	Acts of Love
My Calling	My Future	Daily Struggles
Dangerous Places	What Works	Dating My Spouse
Control	Male Friends	Humility
Turning It Over	One Day at a Time	My Daily God Time
My Worst Moment	The Gift of Recovery	What God is Doing
Addictions in My Family	Breaking the Curse for My Children	

...And any other topic the chairperson feels is appropriate. Remember, don't be graphic, be honest!

Recovery Groups

What are Recovery Groups?

Recovery Groups are Christ-based support groups for people wanting freedom from being driven by addiction.

How do they work?

One person, impressed by the Holy Spirit who desires to assist helping others obtain freedom from being driven by addiction, asks their pastor to sponsor this ministry. This *point person* will be the contact person for the church. The church will refer people who feel driven by their addiction to the *point person*. This *point person* will meet with those desiring help and will cover the *Recovery Principles* and *Recovery Covenant* with them. Once the person agrees to the *Freedom Principles* and *Freedom Covenant*, they are given the group location and time.

Recovery Group Roles

1. The *point person* serves as the contact person for anyone interested in attending the group. This is to protect the group from someone just dropping in unexpectedly. The *point person* can serve for an indefinite amount of time but should be reconsidered after one year of service.

2. The *chairperson* of the meeting is responsible to start the meeting by asking the point man if any new people need to make a Freedom Covenant. If there are no new Recovery Covenants to be addressed, the chairperson starts the introductions and chooses the topic for the group discussion. The *chairperson* serves the group for a maximum of 8 weeks.   At that time, someone else volunteers to chair the meeting.

Recovery Principles for the First 100 Days of Recovery

1. Pray - Pray in the morning asking Jesus to keep you free today.
2. Read - Read the Bible and read recovery-related material.
3. Meetings - Attend every meeting possible.
4. Call - Call someone in your group and check in with that person at the beginning of each day.
5. Pray - Pray in the evening, thanking God for keeping you free today.

One-Year Recovery Covenant

1. The members of the Recovery Group covenant to total confidentiality of all group members and discussions held during group meetings.

2. Members covenant to attend the Recovery Group for one year and to work through the Recovery Materials and report progress to the group.

3. Members covenant to keep the Recovery Principles for the first 100 days of their journey toward freedom.